Atlas of
Paleogeographic Maps
of North America

CHARLES SCHUCHERT, 1858–1942

"Foremost paleogeographer of our time"

Atlas of Paleogeographic Maps of North America

CHARLES SCHUCHERT

With an introduction by

CARL O. DUNBAR

Director
Peabody Museum of Natural History
Yale University

JOHN WILEY & SONS, INC., NEW YORK

CHAPMAN & HALL, LIMITED, LONDON

Library of Congress Catalog Card Number: MAP 55–214

Printed in the United States of America

INTRODUCTION

by Carl O. Dunbar

IN the fall of 1904 Charles Schuchert came to Yale and began teaching his first course in the Stratigraphy of North America. As he later recounted, the experience was at first rather frustrating both to him and to the students. The subject matter seemed to be a welter of details without synthesis. Schuchert tried diluting and simplifying the course, but still he could sense that the boys "were not seeing the forest for the trees." Then he hit upon the idea of using a large blackboard map of the continent on which he could plot each section as it was introduced. The effect on the course was immediate and gratifying.

Thus sensing the potential usefulness of paleogeography as an aid in the study of stratigraphy, he turned to the task of building a set of paleogeographic maps for North America. The first step was to prepare a working base on a size 20 by 22 inches from which maps were printed so that he could use a separate one for each series or subseries of the stratigraphic record. For the next 5 years his time was largely devoted to a search of the literature and the plotting of data that culminated in his *Paleogeography of North America* in 1910.

Schuchert realized that this pioneer effort was only a beginning. Though the general pattern of the paleogeographic history of North America could be seen, many details were missing or insecure. Data were still lacking for large areas of the continent, and correlations were subject to revision in many respects. He had published only 49 maps in 1910, and he realized that each of these represented a span of time so great that it must have embraced important changes in the relations of lands and seas and, therefore, did not accurately represent the paleogeography of any particular moment in geologic history. He believed that with more precise correlation it would eventually

be possible to prepare at least 100 maps and possibly 125.

Being a bachelor, Schuchert made of paleogeography his mistress and constant companion. As the endless stream of stratigraphic papers crossed his desk, some hours of each day and most of his evenings were spent abstracting and plotting data. A special drafting table was built beside his desk with space for more than 100 maps so that new information could be added readily as it came to light, and, in order to facilitate change, the data were plotted in pencil. Most of the maps are now dog-eared and worn, and not a few have been patched or renewed, for they are the result of growth over a long period of years and represent literally the work of a lifetime.

These studies served as the basis of Schuchert's presidential address, *Sites and Nature of North American Geosynclines,* given before the Geological Society of America in 1922, and they were the source for the well-known paleogeographic maps published in several editions of a *Textbook of Historical Geology* by Schuchert and Dunbar and of *Historical Geology* by Dunbar. It was Schuchert's intention to publish the full set of his detailed maps, but during the years of active growth and change the time for publication never seemed to have arrived. After retirement, however, he determined to make a magnum opus of the completion of his paleogeographic maps with accompanying text that would embody all the data upon which they were built. This plan grew into a projected review of the stratigraphy of North America in four volumes, to be followed by an atlas including about 125 maps. The first volume, *Historical Geology of the Antillean-Caribbean Region,* was published in 1935, and the second volume, *Stratigraphy of the Eastern and Central United States,* followed posthumously in 1943. The third volume was largely written but still incomplete and the fourth was in the planning stage when he died in October, 1942. In the meanwhile the maps were under constant study and, as always, were unfinished.

After his passing, it fell to the lot of his faithful secretary, Clara M. LeVene, and the writer to select the best of Professor Schuchert's maps and to arrange for their publication. The long delay is regretted, but it stemmed from various circumstances beyond our control. Since all the maps had to be redrafted in ink, it was decided to prepare a new basemap, and, with the kind permission of the Geological Society of America, one was adapted from the projection used in the latest geologic map of North America. Dr. John Sanders spent many months transferring the data and drafting the maps on this new base. Mrs. Mildred P. Cloud has prepared the index and cared for editorial work involved in the legends.

Each map in the present atlas is faced with a legend indicating, as far as possible, the chief stratigraphic units present in each area of outcrop. On part of his working maps Professor Schuchert left marginal notes indicating the formations involved, but in most of them the list was not inclusive, especially in the remote areas of Canada, Alaska, Mexico, and Central America. Marginal notes in many such instances indicate that Schuchert had faunal data even though the formations were not named. For all such outcrops, where the writer has no certain information as to Professor Schuchert's intentions, the legends are incomplete.

It should be noted that the Williston Basin was discovered after Schuchert's death and that many of the maps will need modification in that area to take account of the new information now available. No attempt has been made to revise the maps or to bring them up to date—they stand as they were at the time of Schuchert's death in October, 1942. The decision to leave them so rests on two considerations. In the first place paleogeography is still in a pioneering stage of rapid growth and change, and to attempt to revise the maps would have led to an endless quest; in the second place, even if time had been available to keep the maps up to date, they would by this time have ceased to be the work of Charles Schuchert. It is believed that they will form a substantial base on which many others can build.

Since a paleogeographic map is designed to show the distribution of lands, and seas, and of areas of sedimentary deposition, at a given time in geologic history, its validity depends largely on the accuracy of the stratigraphic correlations involved. In this connection the Correlation Charts of the Committee on Stratigraphy of the National Research Council will be a very useful, if not an indispensable, aid in checking and revising Schuchert's maps. Several of these charts were available before his death and were extensively used by him. If all had been available when he launched his magnum opus, his labors would have been greatly simplified. These correlation charts have been published in the *Bulletin of the Geological Society of America,* and reprints of individual charts with accompanying text may be secured from the Secretary of the Society as follows:

CHART 1

Cambrian System; by B. F. Howell *et al. G.S.A. Bull.,* v. 55, 1944, pp. 993–1003. Reprints .15

CHART 2

Ordovician System; by W. H. Twenhofel *et al. Ibid.,* v. 65, 1954, pp. 247–298. Reprints .50

CHART 3

Silurian System; by C. K. Swartz *et al. Ibid.,* v. 53, 1942, pp. 533–538. Reprints .15

CHART 4

Devonian System; by G. A. Cooper *et al. Ibid.,* v. 53, 1942, pp. 1729–1794. Reprints .35

CHART 5

Mississippian System; by J. M. Weller *et al. Ibid.,* v. 59, 1948, pp. 91–196. Reprints .50

CHART 6

Pennsylvanian System; by R. C. Moore *et al. Ibid.,* v. 55, 1944, pp. 657–706. Reprints .30

CHART 7

Permian System; by C. O. Dunbar *et al. In preparation.*

CHART 8*a*

Triassic System exclusive of Canada. *In preparation.*

CHART 8*b*

Triassic System in Canada; by F. H. McLearn. *Ibid.,* v. 64, 1953, pp. 1205–1228. Reprints .35

CHART 8c

Jurassic formations exclusive of Canada; by R. W. Imlay. *Ibid.*, v. 63, 1952, pp. 953–992. Reprints .35

CHART 8d

Jurassic formations of Canada; by Hans Frebold. *Ibid.*, v. 64, 1953, pp. 1229–1246. Reprints .35

CHART 9

Cretaceous formations of the Atlantic and Gulf Coastal Plains; by L. W. Stephenson, P. B. King, W. H. Monroe, and R. W. Imlay. *Ibid.*, v. 53, 1942, pp. 435–448. Reprints .25

CHART 10a

Cretaceous formations of the Greater Antilles, Central America, and Mexico; by R. W. Imlay. *Ibid.*, v. 55, 1944, pp. 1005–1045. Reprints .35

CHART 10b

Cretaceous formations of the western interior of the United States; by W. A. Coban and J. B. Reeside, Jr. *Ibid.*, v. 63, 1952, pp. 1011–1044. Reprints .35

CHART 10c

Cretaceous formations of Canada; by F. H. McLearn. *In preparation.*

CHART 10d

Cretaceous formations of Greenland and Alaska; by R. W. Imlay and J. B. Reeside, Jr. *Ibid.*, v. 65, 1954, pp. 223–246. Reprints .35

CHART 10e

Cretaceous formations of the Pacific border; by Willis Popenoe *et al. In preparation.*

CHART 11

Cenozoic formations of western North America; by C. E. Weaver *et al. Ibid.*, v. 55, 1944, pp. 569–598. Reprints .20

CHART 12

Cenozoic formations of the Atlantic and Gulf coastal plains; by C. W. Cooke *et al. Ibid.*, v. 54, 1943, pp. 1713–1723. Reprints .15

References Cited

Schuchert, Charles, 1910, Paleogeography of North America, *Geol. Soc. Am. Bull.*, v. 20, pp. 427–606, pl. 46–101.

Schuchert, Charles, 1923, Sites and nature of the North American geosynclines, *ibid.*, v. 34, pp. 151–230.

Schuchert, Charles, 1935, *Historical geology of the Antillean-Caribbean region*, p. 1–811, New York, John Wiley & Sons.

Schuchert, Charles, 1943, *Stratigraphy of the eastern and central United States*, pp. 1–1013, New York, John Wiley & Sons.

Schuchert, Charles, and C. O. Dunbar, *Textbook of historical geology*, New York, John Wiley & Sons, 3rd ed., 1933; 4th ed., 1941.

CONTENTS

KEY TO MAPS

Marine waters on areas now on continent (outcrops in black)

Areas of nonmarine deposition (outcrops in black)

Outcrops of nonmarine strata, area of deposition not shown

Jurassic intrusives

Areas of Permian evaporites

Location of well

Indicates volcanic activity

Shoreline (dashed where doubtful)

1

Lower Cambrian

Basal Waucoban

STRATIGRAPHIC UNITS REPRESENTED

APPALACHIAN TROUGH—Unicoi group and equivalents

CALIFORNIA—Campito ss.

NEVADA—Campito ss.

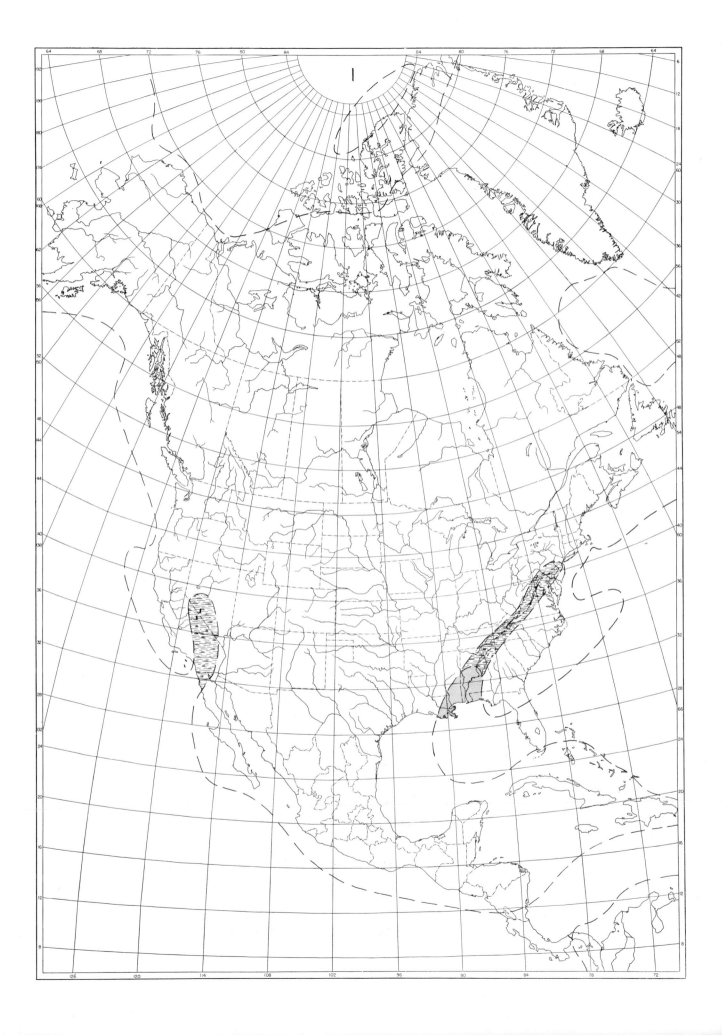

2

Lower Cambrian
Middle Waucoban

STRATIGRAPHIC UNITS REPRESENTED

ALABAMA—Weisner fm. to Shady dol.

CALIFORNIA—Johnnie fm. and Stirling qtzite.

NEVADA—Prospect Mountain qtzite.

NEW JERSEY—Hardyston qtzite.

NEW YORK—Bomoseen fm. and Nassau beds

PENNSYLVANIA—Antietam ss., Harpers sh., and Tomstown dol.

TENNESSEE—Erwin qtzite., Hampton sh., and Shady dol.

UTAH—Prospect Mountain qtzite.

VERMONT—Monkton qtzite. and Winooski marble

VIRGINIA—Antietam ss., Harpers sh., and Tomstown dol.

———

BRITISH COLUMBIA—Mahto fm. and Tah fm.

GREENLAND—Wulff River fm.

LABRADOR—Bradore fm.

NEWFOUNDLAND—Bradore fm. and Cloud Mountain gr.

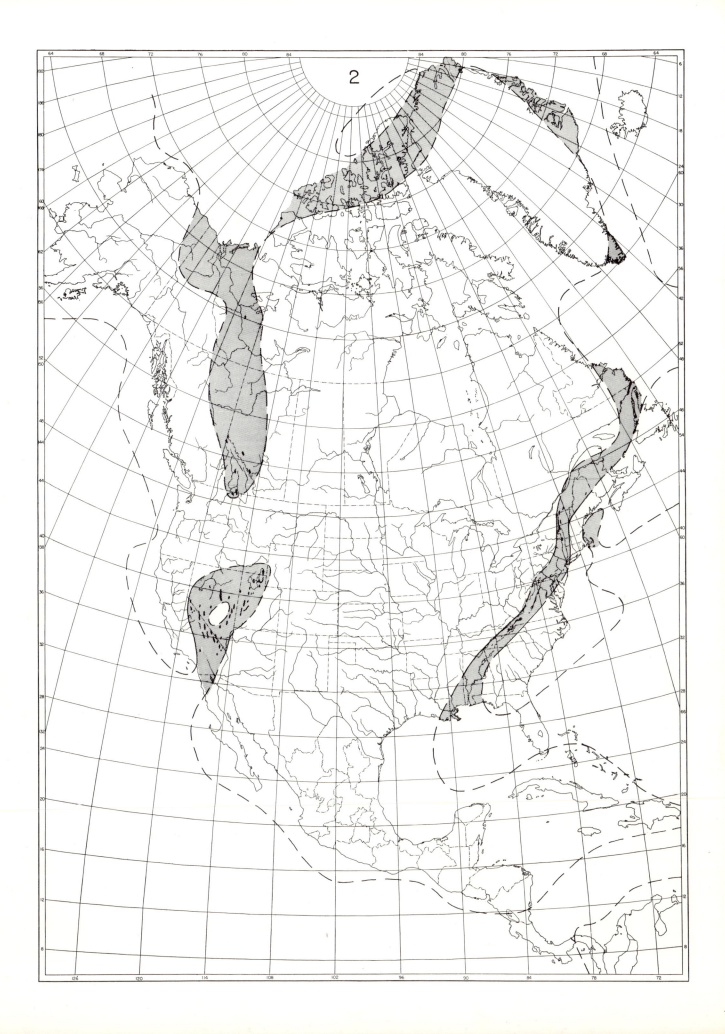

2

3

Lower Cambrian
High Waucoban

STRATIGRAPHIC UNITS REPRESENTED

ALABAMA—Rome fm.

CALIFORNIA—Wood Canyon fm.

GEORGIA—Rome fm.

NEVADA—Pioche sh. and Tatow ls.

NEW YORK—Schodack sh. of Champlain Valley

NORTH CAROLINA—Rome fm.

PENNSYLVANIA—Waynesboro fm.

TENNESSEE—Rome fm.

UTAH—Pioche sh. and Tatow ls.

VERMONT—Mallett dol. and Parker sh.

VIRGINIA—Rome fm.

———

BRITISH COLUMBIA—Hota fm. of Robson Peak, St. Piran fm., and Mount Whyte fm.

GREENLAND, NW.—Cape Kent fm., Wulff River fm. (upper part)

LABRADOR—Devil's Cove fm., Forteau fm., Hawke Bay fm.

NEW BRUNSWICK—Hanford Brook fm., Ratcliff Brook fm.

NEWFOUNDLAND—Devil's Cove fm., Forteau fm., Hawkes Bay fm.

NEWFOUNDLAND, SE.—Brigus fm.

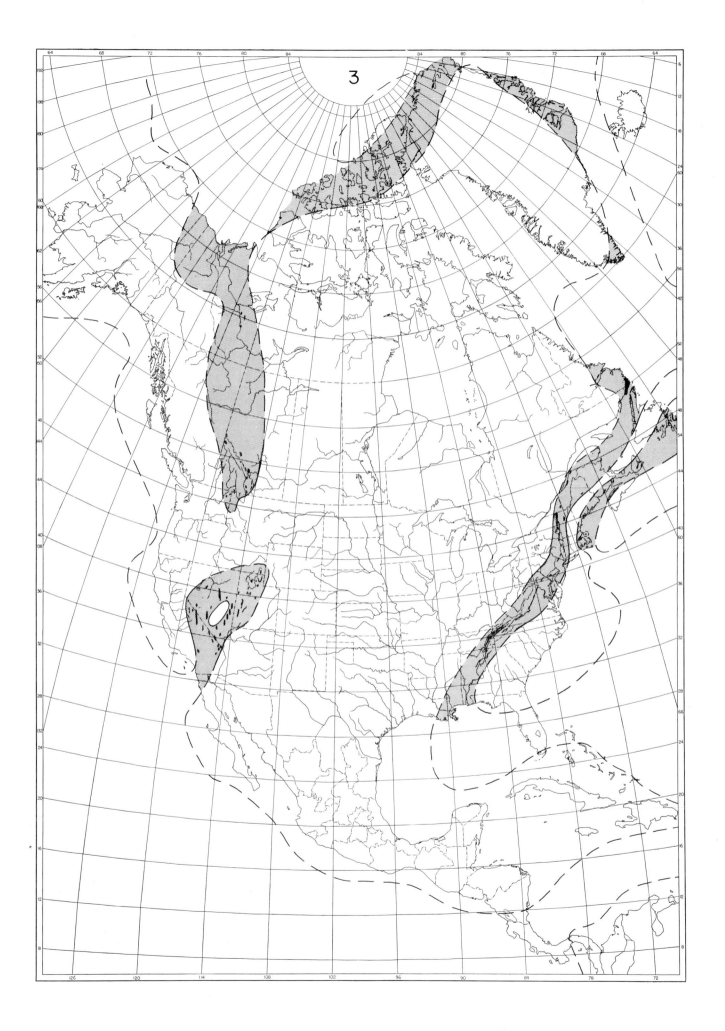

4

Middle Cambrian
Basal Acadian

STRATIGRAPHIC UNITS REPRESENTED

ALABAMA—Conasauga sh. (lower part)

ARIZONA—Bolsa qtzite. and Pima fm. (lower part)

GEORGIA—Conasauga sh. (lower part)

MARYLAND—Elbrook fm. (lower part)

MONTANA—Flathead ss., Gordon sh., and Wolsey sh.

NEVADA—Chisholm sh., Comet sh., Eldorado ls. (lower part), and Lyndon fm.

PENNSYLVANIA—Elbrook fm. (lower part)

TENNESSEE—Conasauga sh. (lower part) and Rutledge ls.

UTAH—Brigham qtzite., Howell ls., Langston fm., and Ute sh.

VIRGINIA—Conasauga sh. (lower part), Elbrook fm. (lower part), and Rutledge ls.

WYOMING—Depass fm. (lower part), Flathead ss., and Gros Ventre fm. (lower part)

BRITISH COLUMBIA—Cathedral dol., Chetang fm., Ptarmigan fm., and Tatei fm.

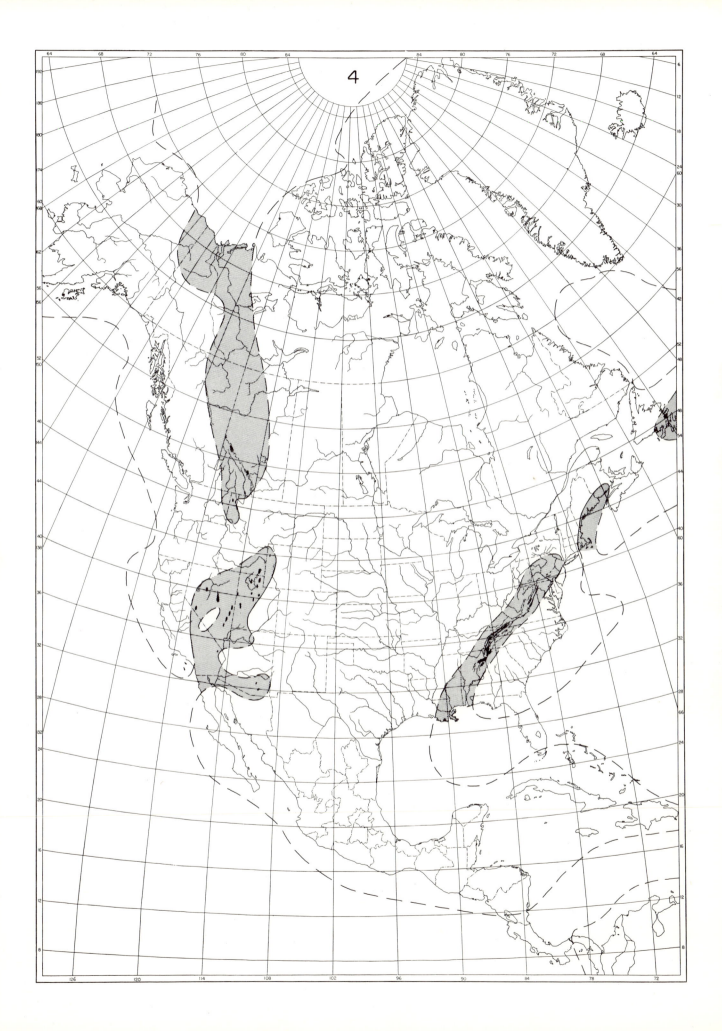

5

Middle Cambrian
Upper Acadian

STRATIGRAPHIC UNITS REPRESENTED

ARIZONA—Cochise fm. and Pima fm. (upper part)

CALIFORNIA—Bonanza King fm. and Cornfield Springs fm.

MARYLAND—Elbrook fm. (middle part)

MASSACHUSETTS—Braintree sl.

MONTANA—Depass fm. (upper part), Gros Ventre fm. (upper part), Meagher fm., Pagoda ls., Park fm., Pentagon sh., Steamboat ls., and Switchback fm.

NEVADA—Eldorado dol. (upper part), Geddes ls., Highland Peak ls., and Secret Canyon sh.

PENNSYLVANIA—Elbrook fm. (middle part) and Pleasant Hill ls.

TENNESSEE—Conasauga sh. (middle part), Maryville ls., and Rogersville sh.

UTAH—Blacksmith fm., Bloomington fm., Marjum fm., Swasey fm., and Wheeler fm.

VERMONT—Rugg Brook dol. and St. Albans sl.

VIRGINIA—Conasauga sh. (middle part), Elbrook fm. (middle part), Maryville ls., and Rogersville sh.

WYOMING—Depass fm. (upper part), Gros Ventre fm. (upper part), Meagher fm., and Park fm.

———

BRITISH COLUMBIA—Eldon dol., Stephen fm., and Titkana fm.

GREENLAND—Pemmican River fm.

NEW BRUNSWICK—Fossil Brook fm., Hastings Cove fm., and Porter Road fm.

NEWFOUNDLAND—Cape Wood fm., Chamberlin's Brook fm., Killigrew Brook fm., Long Pond fm., and March Point fm.

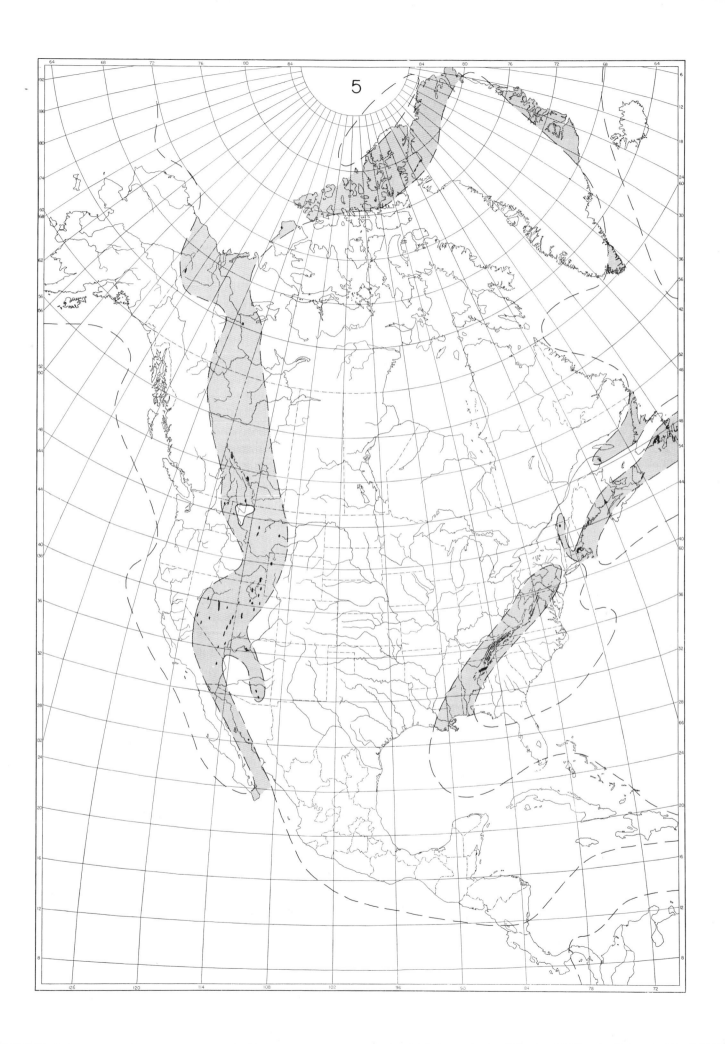

6

Upper Cambrian
Dresbachian

STRATIGRAPHIC UNITS REPRESENTED

ALABAMA—Nolichucky sh. and Maynardsville ls.

ARKANSAS—Bonneterre dol. and Lamotte ss.

ARIZONA—Peppersauce Canyon ss.

COLORADO—Sawatch fm.

MINNESOTA—Dresbach stage

MISSOURI—Bonneterre dol. and Lamotte ss.

MONTANA—Du Noir memb., Maurice memb., and Pilgrim fm. (lower part)

NEVADA—Mendha ls. (lower part)

NEW JERSEY—Kittatinny fm. (lower part)

NEW YORK—Potsdam ss.

OKLAHOMA—Reagan ss.

PENNSYLVANIA—Conococheague ls. (basal part) and Warrior fm.

SOUTH DAKOTA—Deadwood fm. (lower part) of Black Hills

TENNESSEE—Nolichucky sh.

TEXAS—Cap Mountain fm.

UTAH—Nounan fm., Orr fm., Warm Creek fm., and Weeks fm.

VERMONT—Hungerford fm. and Rockledge cgl.

VIRGINIA—Conococheague ls. (basal part)

WISCONSIN—Dresbach stage

WYOMING—Du Noir memb., Maurice memb., and Pilgrim fm. (lower part)

———

ALBERTA—Bosworth fm., Lynx fm., and Sullivan fm.

BRITISH COLUMBIA—Bosworth fm., Lynx fm., and Sullivan fm.

GASPÉ—Murphy's Creek fm.

NEWFOUNDLAND—Petit Jardin fm.

Editor's note: Dashed line in Texas, and from Nebraska to Michigan, indicates limits of the earliest Upper Cambrian seaway.

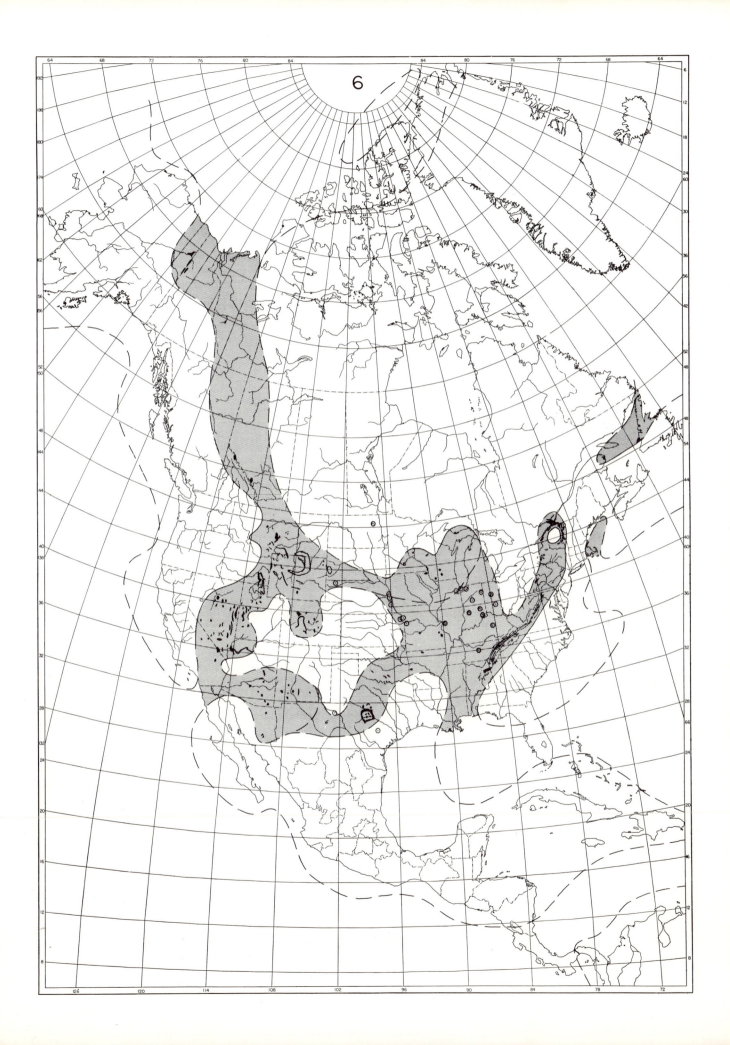

6

7

Upper Cambrian
Franconian

STRATIGRAPHIC UNITS REPRESENTED

ALABAMA—Copper Ridge dol. (lower part)

ARIZONA—Copper Queen fm.

CALIFORNIA—Nopah fm.

GEORGIA—Copper Ridge dol.

MARYLAND—Conococheague ls. (middle part)

MICHIGAN—Munising ss.

MINNESOTA—Franconia stage

MISSOURI—Davis dol., Derby dol., and Doe Run dol. of Ozark region

MONTANA—Pilgrim ls. (middle part) and Snowy Range fm.

NEVADA—Goodwin ls. and Mendha ls. (middle part)

NEW JERSEY—Kittatinny fm. (middle part)

NEW YORK—Hoyt ls. and Theresa fm.

OKLAHOMA—Fort Sill ls. and Honey Creek fm. of Arbuckle region

PENNSYLVANIA—Conococheague ls. (middle part), Frederick ls. (middle part), and Gatesburg ls. (lower part)

SOUTH DAKOTA—Deadwood fm. (middle part) of Black Hills

TENNESSEE—Copper Ridge dol. (lower part)

TEXAS, central—Wilberns fm. (lower part)

UTAH—St. Charles fm. (lower part)

VIRGINIA—Conococheague ls. (middle part) and Copper Ridge dol. (lower part)

WISCONSIN—Franconia stage

WYOMING—Pilgrim ls. (middle part) and Snowy Range fm.

————

BRITISH COLUMBIA—Lyell fm. (lower part) and Lynx fm. (middle part)

NEW BRUNSWICK—Narrows fm.

NEWFOUNDLAND—Elliott Cove sh.

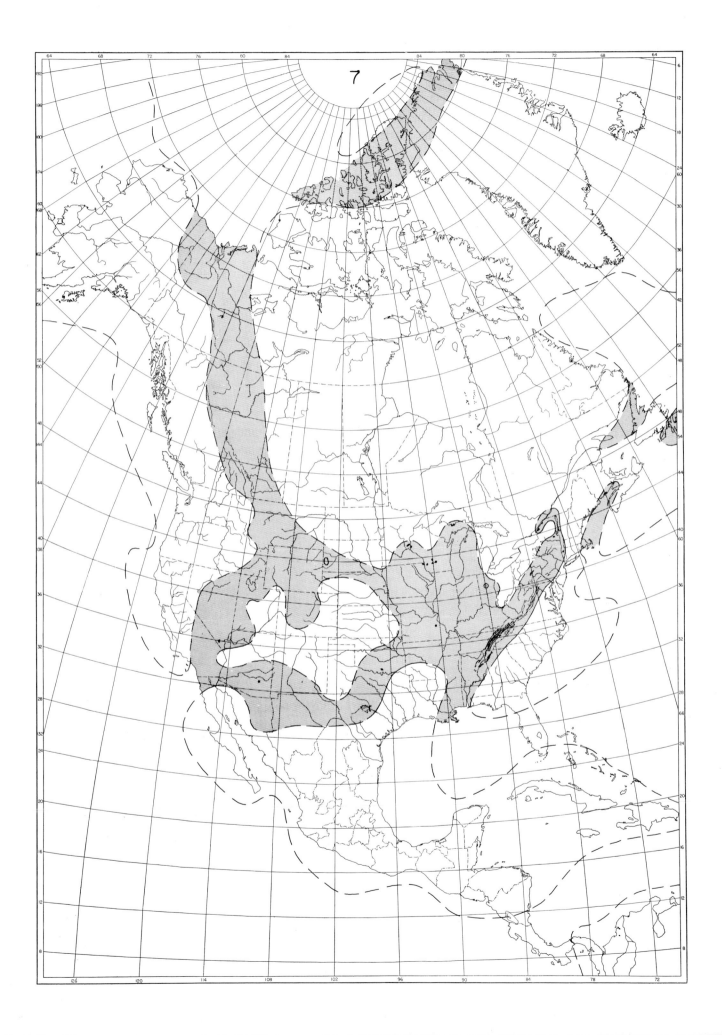

7

8

Upper Cambrian
Trempealeauian

STRATIGRAPHIC UNITS REPRESENTED

ALABAMA—Copper Ridge dol. (upper part)

ARIZONA—Rincon ls.

ARKANSAS—Eminence dol. and Potosi dol. of Ozark region

CALIFORNIA—Nopah fm. (upper part)

COLORADO—Peerless fm. (upper part)

GEORGIA—Copper Ridge dol. (upper part)

MARYLAND—Conococheague ls. (upper part)

MINNESOTA—Trempealeau stage

MISSOURI—Eminence dol. and Potosi dol. of Ozark region

MONTANA—Grove Creek fm.

NEVADA—Pogonip ls. (lower part)

NEW YORK—Little Falls dol.

OKLAHOMA—Signal Mountain ls.

PENNSYLVANIA—Conococheague ls. (upper part) and Gatesburg fm. (Mines memb.)

SOUTH DAKOTA—Deadwood fm. (upper part) of Black Hills

TENNESSEE—Copper Ridge dol. (upper part)

TEXAS—Ellenburger ls. (lower part) and Wilberns fm. (upper part)

UTAH—Notch Peak fm. (upper part)

VERMONT—Gorge fm.

VIRGINIA—Conococheague ls. (upper part) and Copper Ridge dol. (upper part)

WISCONSIN—Trempealeau stage

WYOMING—Grove Creek fm.

———————

BRITISH COLUMBIA—Goodsir fm. (upper part), Lyell fm. (upper part), and Lynx fm. (upper part)

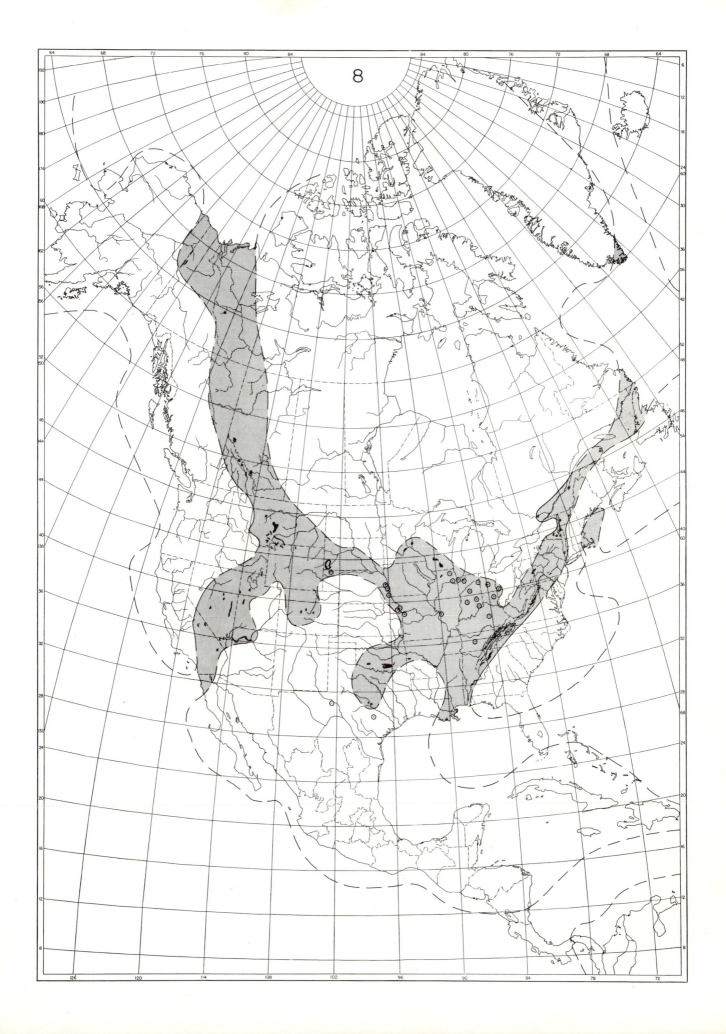

9

Lower Ordovician
Lower Canadian

STRATIGRAPHIC UNITS REPRESENTED

ALABAMA—Chepultepec ls.

ARIZONA—Longfellow ls. (upper part)

MARYLAND—Knox dol. (basal part), Larke dol., and Stonehenge ls.

MINNESOTA—Oneota dol.

MISSOURI—Gasconade dol. of Ozark region

NEVADA—Pogonip ls. (part)

NEW YORK—Schaghticoke sh. and Tribes Hill ls.

OKLAHOMA—Crystal Mountain ss. of the Ouachita Mountains and McKenzie Hill fm. of Arbuckle region

PENNSYLVANIA—Larke dol. and Stonehenge ls.

TENNESSEE—Chepultepec ls. and Knox dol. (basal part)

TEXAS, central—Tanyard fm.

TEXAS, TRANS-PECOS—Bliss ss. and Marathon ls. (basal part)

UTAH—Garden City ls. (lower part)

VERMONT—Corliss cgl., Grandge sh., and Highgate sl.

VIRGINIA—Chepultepec ls., Larke dol., and Stonehenge ls.

WISCONSIN—Oneota dol.

———

CANADIAN ROCKIES—Mons fm.

GREENLAND—Cape Clay fm. and Cass Fjord fm.

NEW BRUNSWICK—Bretonian gr. (lower part) and Browns Mountain gr. (lower part)

NEWFOUNDLAND, SE.—Clarenville sh.

NEWFOUNDLAND, W.—Green Point sh. and St. George dol. (lower part)

NOVA SCOTIA—Bretonian gr. (lower part) and Browns Mountain gr. (lower part)

ONTARIO—March dol., Nepean ss., and Oxford dol. of Ottawa area

QUEBEC—Levis sh. (lower part) and Morgan Corners ls., Strites Pond ls., and Wallace Creek ls. of Phillipsburg area.

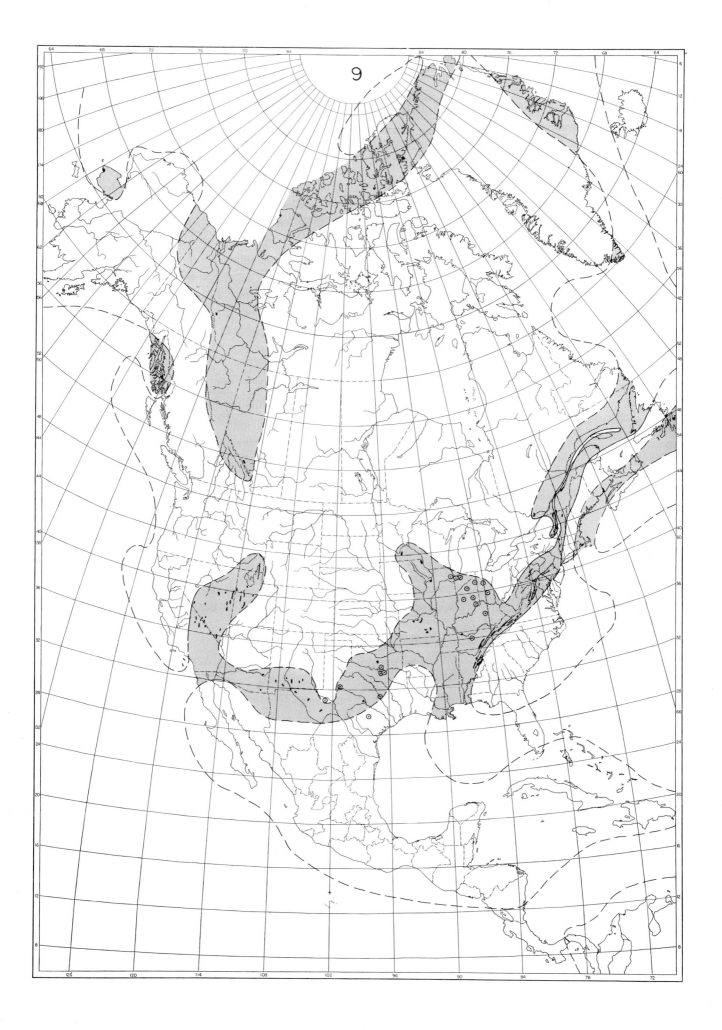

10

Lower Ordovician
Middle Canadian

STRATIGRAPHIC UNITS REPRESENTED

ALABAMA—Longview ls. and Newala ls.

COLORADO—Manitou fm. (upper part)

GEORGIA—Longview ls. and Newala ls.

IDAHO—Ramshorn sl.

MARYLAND—Knox dol. (upper part) and Nittany dol.

MINNESOTA—New Richmond ss. and Shakopee dol.

MISSOURI—Cotter dol., Jefferson City fm., and Powell fm. of Ozark region

NEVADA—Pogonip ls. (middle part) and Yellow Hill ls.

NEW YORK—Beekmantown dol. (lower part of Div. D), Deepkill sh. (part), and Ogdensburg dol. of St. Lawrence Valley

OKLAHOMA—Blakely ss. and Mazarn sh. of Ouachita Mountains; Cool Creek fm. and Kindblade fm. of Arbuckle region

PENNSYLVANIA—Nittany dol.

TENNESSEE—Kingsport ls., Longview ls., Mascot dol., and Newala ls.

TEXAS, TRANS-PECOS—El Paso fm. (part) and Marathon ls. (part)

UTAH—Garden City fm. (middle part)

VIRGINIA—Knox dol. (upper part) and Nittany dol.

WISCONSIN—New Richmond ss. and Shakopee dol.

———

CANADIAN ROCKIES—Glenogle sh. and Sarbach ls.

GREENLAND, NW.—Cape Weber fm. and Poulsen Cliff sh.

NEW BRUNSWICK—Bretonia gr. (upper part and Browns Mountain gr. (upper part)

NEWFOUNDLAND, W.—St. George dol. (middle part)

NEWFOUNDLAND, central—Snooks Arm fm.

NEWFOUNDLAND, SE.—Belle Isle ss. and Wabana sh.

NOVA SCOTIA—Bretonia gr. (upper part) and Browns Mountain gr. (upper part)

QUEBEC—Levis sh. (part), Luke Hill ls., and Naylor Ledge fm. of Phillipsburg area

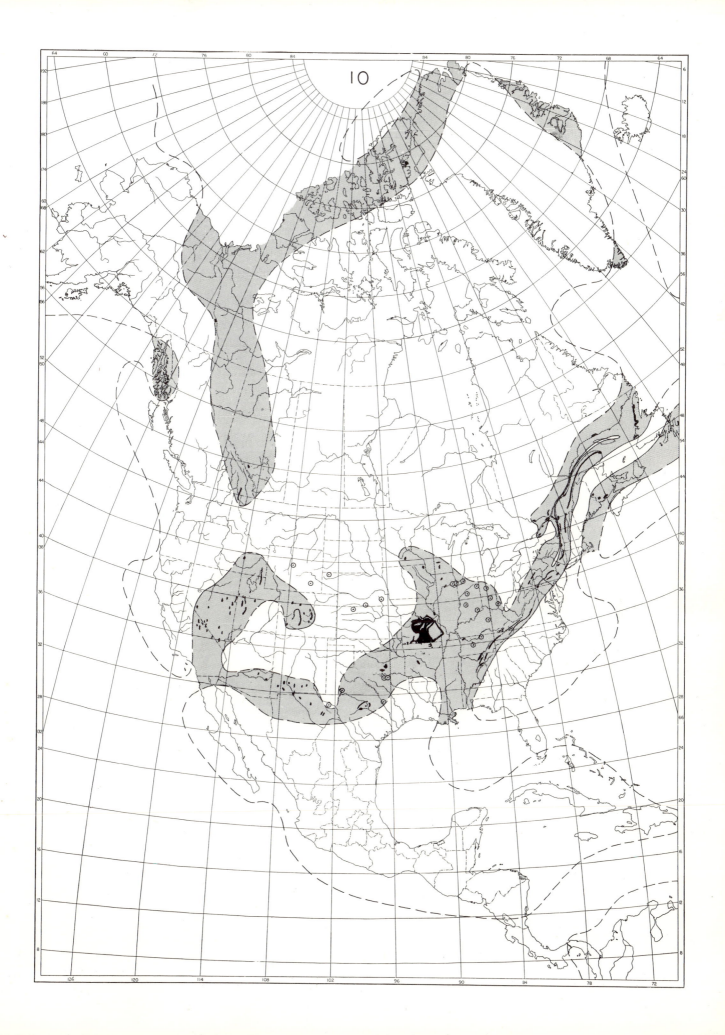

11

Lower Ordovician
Upper Canadian

STRATIGRAPHIC UNITS REPRESENTED

ALABAMA—Odenville ls.

ARKANSAS—Black Rock ls. and Smithville ls. of Ozark region
Ozark region

NEVADA—Pogonip ls. (part)

NEW YORK—Beekmantown dol. (Div. D [part] and E) = Cassin
fm. of Champlain Valley and Deepkill sh. (part)

OKLAHOMA—West Spring Creek ls. of Arbuckle region

PENNSYLVANIA—Axemann ls. and Bellefonte dol.

UTAH—Garden City ls. (upper part)

———

CANADIAN ROCKIES—Sarbach ls. (upper part)

GREENLAND—Cape Weber fm. and Cape Webster fm. (lower
part)

NEWFOUNDLAND—St. George dol. (upper part) and Snooks Arm
gr. (upper part)

QUEBEC—Basswood Creek ls. and Corey ls. of Phillipsburg area

Editor's note: Outcrops in southern Missouri are not shown.

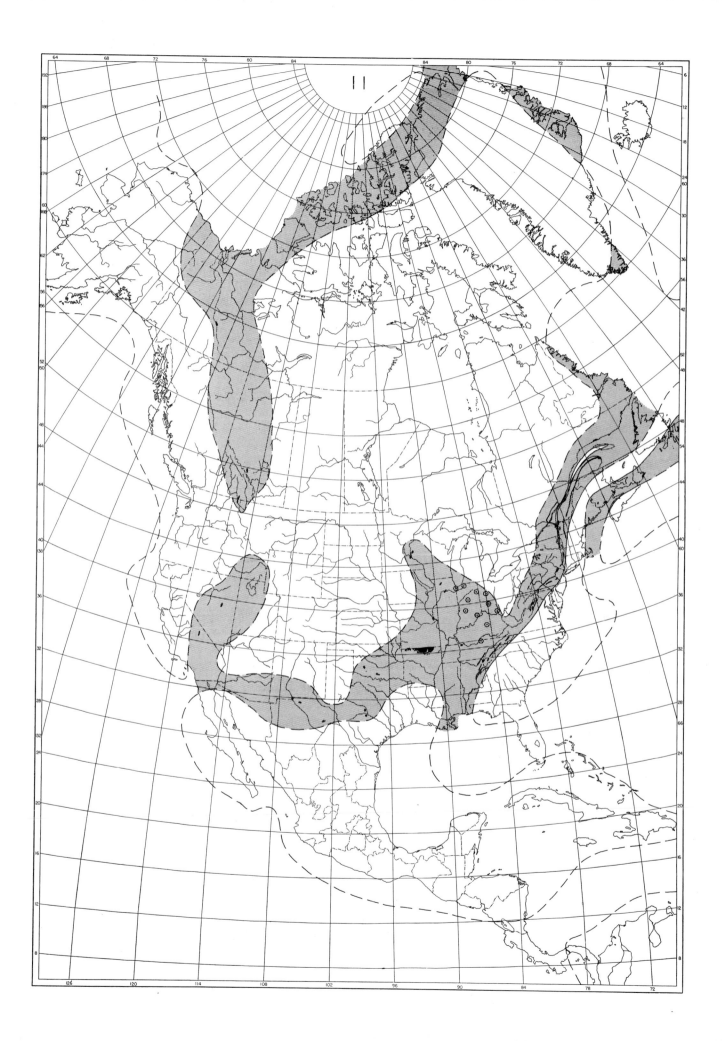

12

Middle Ordovician
Lower Chazyan

STRATIGRAPHIC UNITS REPRESENTED

ALABAMA—Lenoir ls.

ARKANSAS—St. Peter ss.

GEORGIA—Lenoir ls.

NEW YORK—Crown Point ls. and Day Point ls. of Champlain Valley, and Deepkill sh. (upper part)

OKLAHOMA—Joins ls., McLish ls., and Oil Creek ls. of Arbuckle region

TENNESSEE—Blackford fm. and Lenoir ls.

UTAH—Swan Peak qtzite.

VIRGINIA—Blackford fm., Lenoir ls., and New Market ls.

———

ALASKA—Tatina gr. (part)

CANADIAN ROCKIES—Skoki ls.

QUEBEC—Levis sh. (upper part)

Editor's note: Outcrops in the Canadian Rockies and the Yukon Valley of Alaska may be of Black River age.

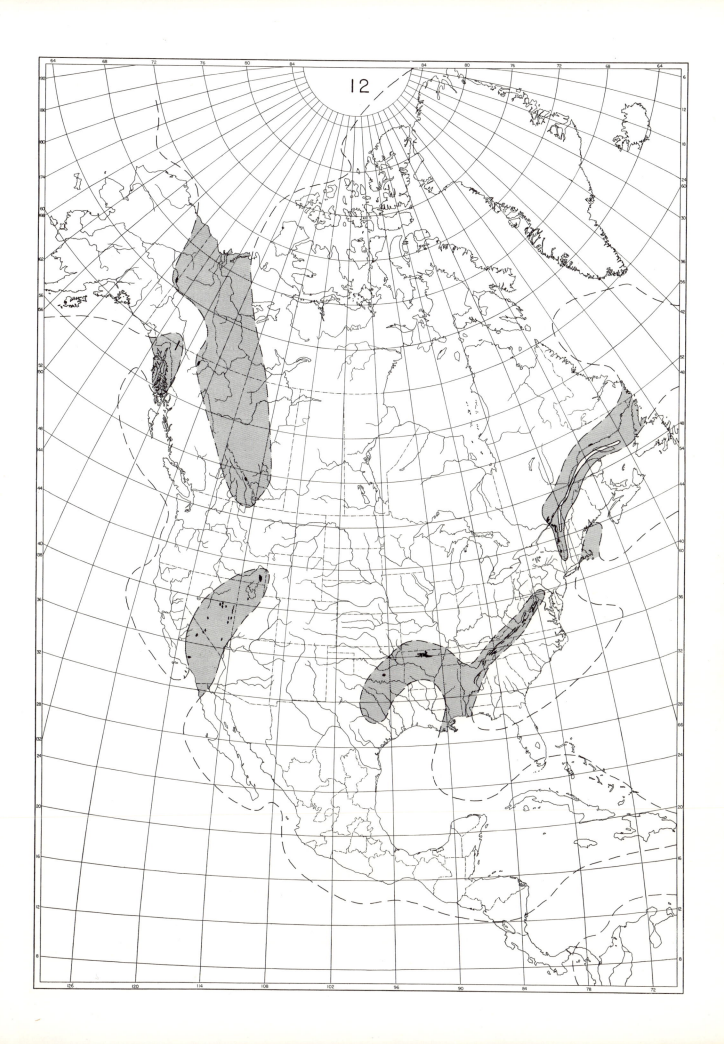

13
Middle Ordovician
Upper Chazyan

STRATIGRAPHIC UNITS REPRESENTED

ALABAMA—Lenoir ls. (upper part) and Lincolnshire ls.

ILLINOIS—St. Peter ss.

INDIANA—St. Peter ss.

IOWA—St. Peter ss.

MINNESOTA—St. Peter ss.

MISSOURI—St. Peter ss.

NEW YORK—Valcour ls. of Champlain Valley

OHIO—St. Peter ss.

OKLAHOMA—St. Peter ss. of Mississippi Valley and Tulip Creek ls. of Arbuckle Mountains

PENNSYLVANIA—Lincolnshire ls.

TENNESSEE—Lincolnshire ls.

WISCONSIN—St. Peter ss.

Editor's note: The outcrop in the Canadian Rockies, based on "Normanskill graptolites," is probably of Black River age.

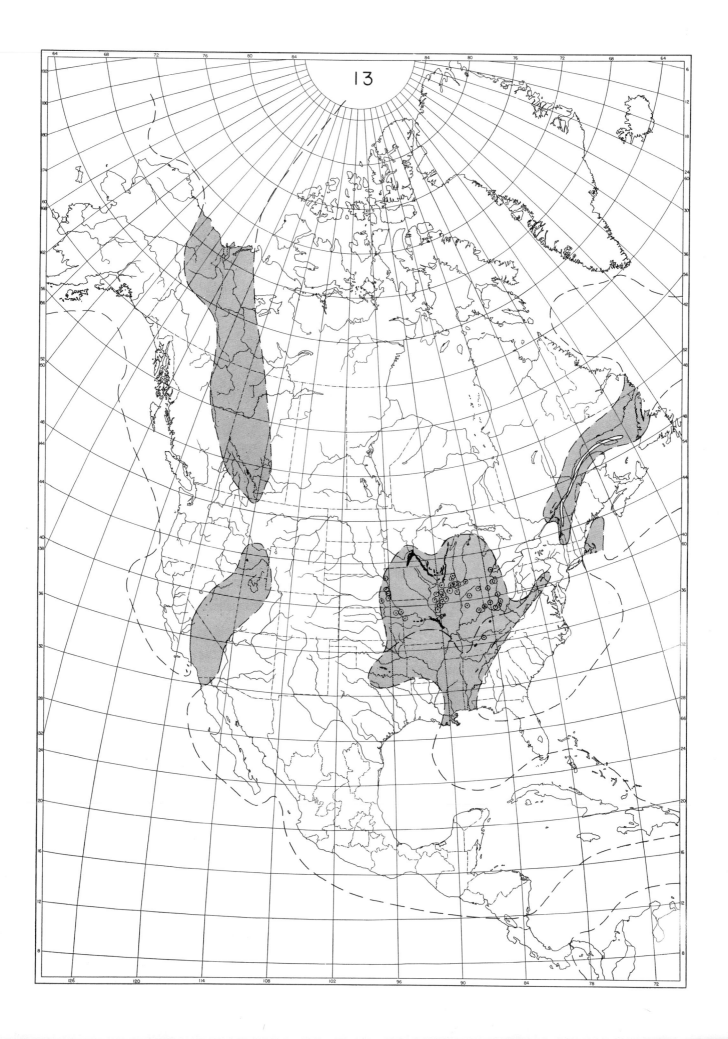

13

14

Middle Ordovician
Black River

STRATIGRAPHIC UNITS REPRESENTED

ALABAMA—Lebanon ls. and Ridley ls.

COLORADO—Harding ss.

ILLINOIS—Platteville fm.

MISSOURI—Platteville fm.

NEW YORK—Chaumont fm., Lowville ls., and Pamelia ls.

OKLAHOMA—Bromide fm.

PENNSYLVANIA—Hatter ls. and Hunter ls.

TENNESSEE—Athens sh., Lebanon ls. and Ridley ls. of Nashville Basin, "Upper Lenoir" ls., Ottosee sh., Sevier fm., and Whitesburg ls.

VERMONT—Chaumont fm. and Lowville ls.

VIRGINIA—Edinburg ls. and Ward Cove ls. to Witten ls.

———

GREENLAND, NW.—Gonioceras Bay fm.

NEWFOUNDLAND, north-central—Exploits Bay gr. (upper part)

NEWFOUNDLAND, W.—Long Point fm.

Editor's note: Outcrops in upper Mississippi Valley also include Spechts Ferry shale, Auburn chert, "Decorah" shale, all of which are now classified as lower Trenton. The Harding sandstone of Colorado is also probably Trentonian.

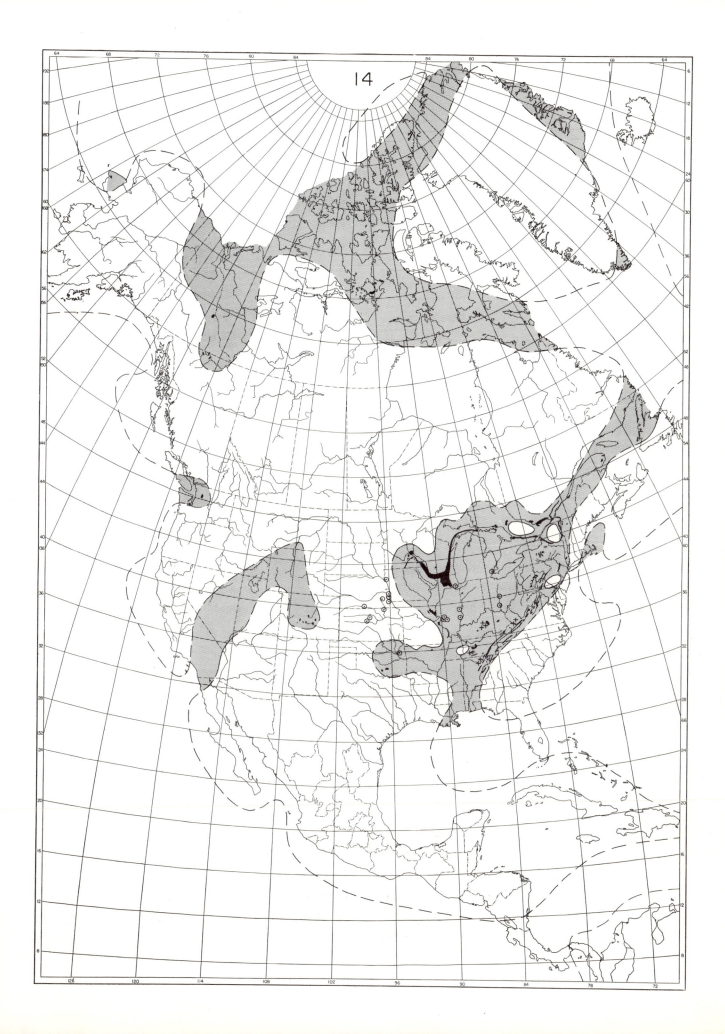

15

Middle Ordovician
Lower and Middle Trenton

STRATIGRAPHIC UNITS REPRESENTED

ARKANSAS—Kimmswick ls.

CALIFORNIA—Barrel Spring fm. [may be late Trenton]

ILLINOIS—Decorah sh. and Galena ls. (lower part)

IOWA—Decorah sh. and Galena ls. (lower part)

KENTUCKY—Lexington ls.

MARYLAND—Martinsburg sh. (lower part)

MINNESOTA—Prosser ls.

MISSOURI—Decorah sh. and Kimmswick ls.

NEVADA—Eureka qtz.

NEW JERSEY—Jacksonburg ls.

NEW YORK—Amsterdam ls., Isle La Motte marble, and Glens Falls ls. and Stony Point sh. of Champlain Valley, Canajoharie sh. and Schenectady flags. of Mohawk Valley, Normanskill sh. (upper part) and Snake Hill sh. of Hudson Valley, Rockland fm. to Sherman Fall ls.

OKLAHOMA—Bigfork chert and Viola ls.

PENNSYLVANIA—Nealmont ls. and Salona ls.

TENNESSEE—Hermitage fm. to Cannon ls. of Nashville Basin and Martinsburg sh. (lower part)

TEXAS, TRANS-PECOS—Woods Hollow sh.

VIRGINIA—Martinsburg sh. (lower part), [Bay fm., Moccasin ls., and Eggleston fm.]

WISCONSIN—Decorah sh. and Galena ls. (lower part)

———

CANADIAN ROCKIES—Wonah qtzite. [probably Upper Ordovician]

GASPÉ—Mictaw sl. (middle part)

NEWFOUNDLAND—Humber Arm gr. (part)

ONTARIO—Rockland ls. to Sherman Fall ls., and Ottawa ls.

QUEBEC—Mystic cgl. and Stanbridge sl. (lower part) of Phillipsburg area

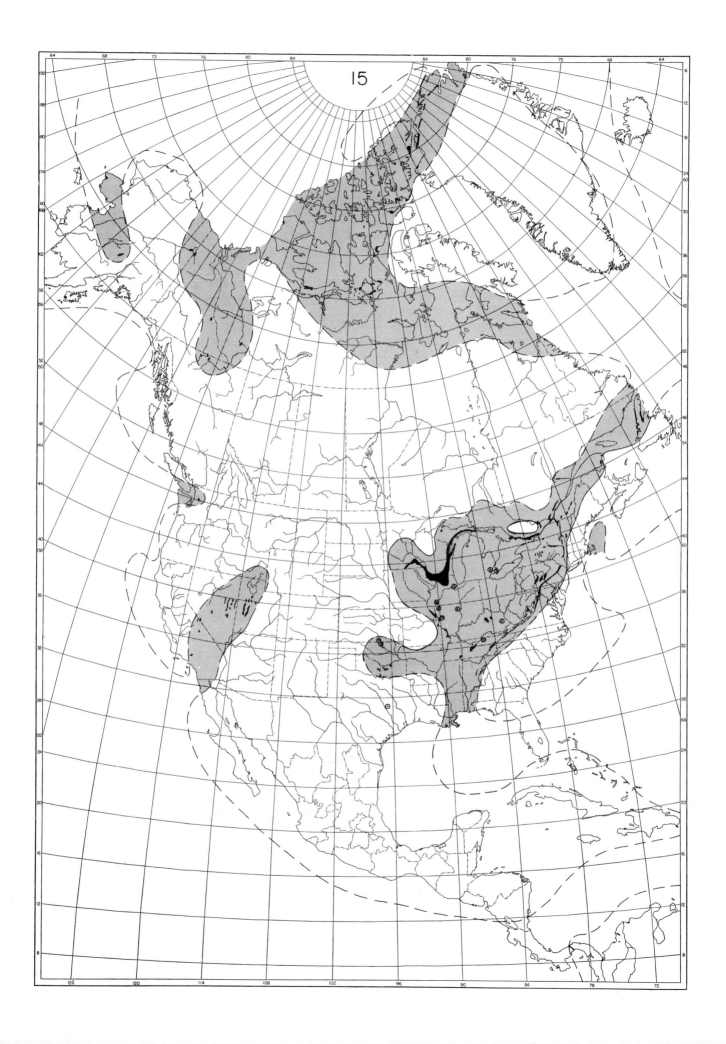

15

16

Middle Ordovician

Highest Trenton

STRATIGRAPHIC UNITS REPRESENTED

KENTUCKY—Cynthiana ls.

MARYLAND—Martinsburg sh. (middle part)

NEW YORK—Atwater Creek sh., Cobourg ls., and Deer River sh., Iberville sh. of Champlain Valley, Utica sh. of Mohawk Valley

OKLAHOMA—Bigfork chert (upper part) of Ouachita Mountains, and Viola ls. (upper part) of Arbuckle region

PENNSYLVANIA—Antes sh. and Martinsburg sh. (middle part)

VIRGINIA—Martinsburg sh. (middle part)

TENNESSEE—Martinsburg sh. (middle part), Cannon ls. (upper part), and Catheys ls. of Nashville Basin

---

ANTICOSTI ISLAND—Makasti sh.

GASPÉ—Mictaw sh. (upper part)

ONTARIO—Collingwood sh.

QUEBEC—Farnham fm. and Stanbridge sl. (upper part) of Phillipsburg area

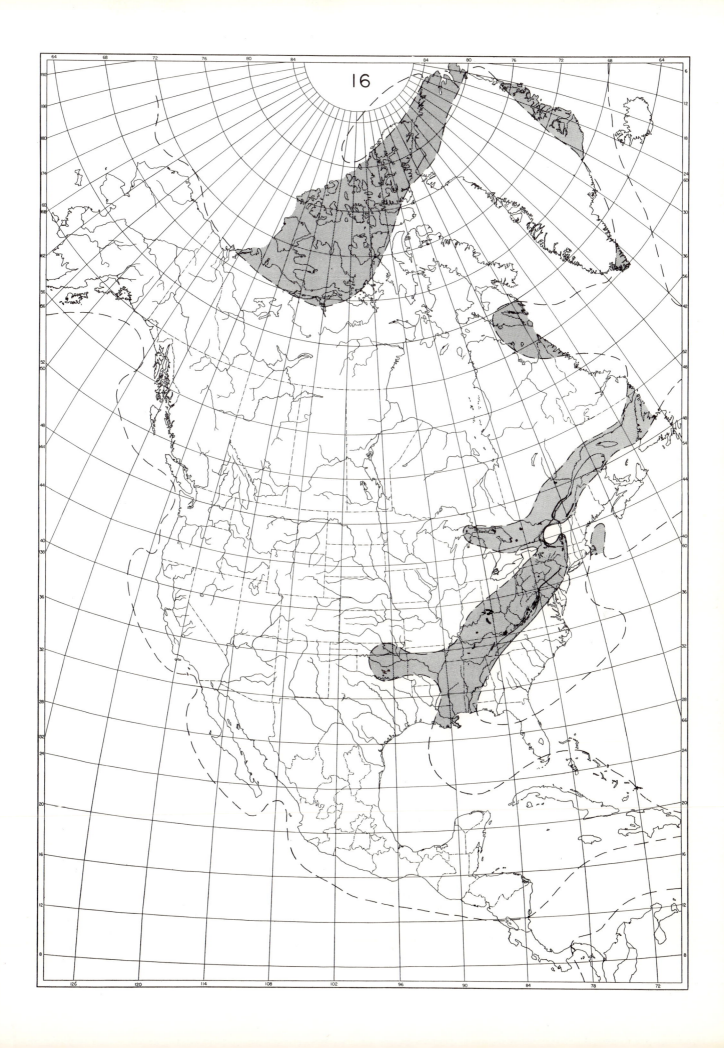

17

Upper Ordovician
Edenian

STRATIGRAPHIC UNITS REPRESENTED

ARKANSAS—Polk Creek sh.

KENTUCKY—Eden gr. of Cincinnati Arch, Fulton sh., Garrard ss., and Million sh.

MARYLAND—Martinsburg sh. (part)

NEW YORK—Indian Ladder sh. of Mohawk Valley, Frankfort sh., and Whetstone Gulf sh.

OHIO—Eden gr. of Cincinnati Arch

PENNSYLVANIA—Reedsville sh. and Martinsburg sh. (part)

VIRGINIA—Martinsburg sh. (part)

———

ONTARIO—Dundas sh. and Wekwemikongsing sh. (lower part)

QUEBEC—Carlsbad sh.

Editor's note: The Polk Creek shale of Arkansas is now classified as Richmondian.

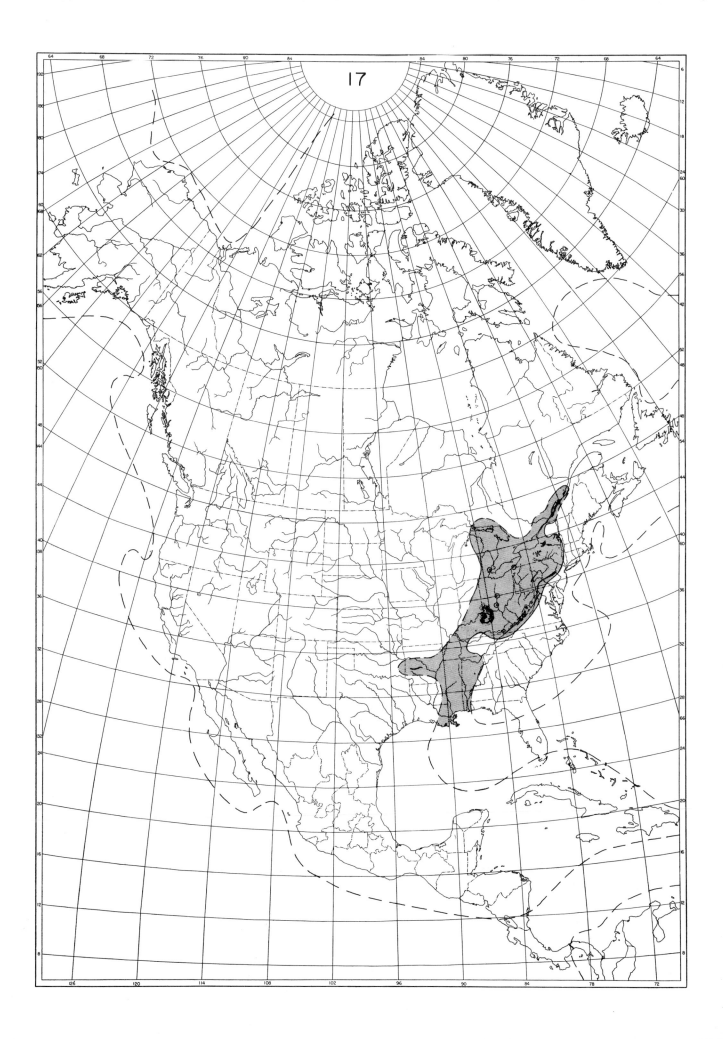

17

18

Upper Ordovician
Maysvillian

STRATIGRAPHIC UNITS REPRESENTED

ARKANSAS—Polk Creek sh.

KENTUCKY—Maysville gr. of Cincinnati Arch

MARYLAND—Martinsburg sh. (upper part)

NEW JERSEY—Shochary ss.

NEW YORK—Pulaski ss. and Oswego ss.

OHIO—Maysville gr. of Cincinnati Arch

PENNSYLVANIA—Bald Eagle ss., Martinsburg sh. (upper part), Reedsville sh. (upper part) and Oswego ss.

TENNESSEE—Leipers sh. of Nashville Basin

VIRGINIA—Martinsburg sh. (upper part) and Reedsville sh. (upper part)

———

ONTARIO—Dundas sh. (upper part) and Wekwemikongsing sh. (upper part)

Editor's note: The Polk Creek shale is now classified as Richmondian.

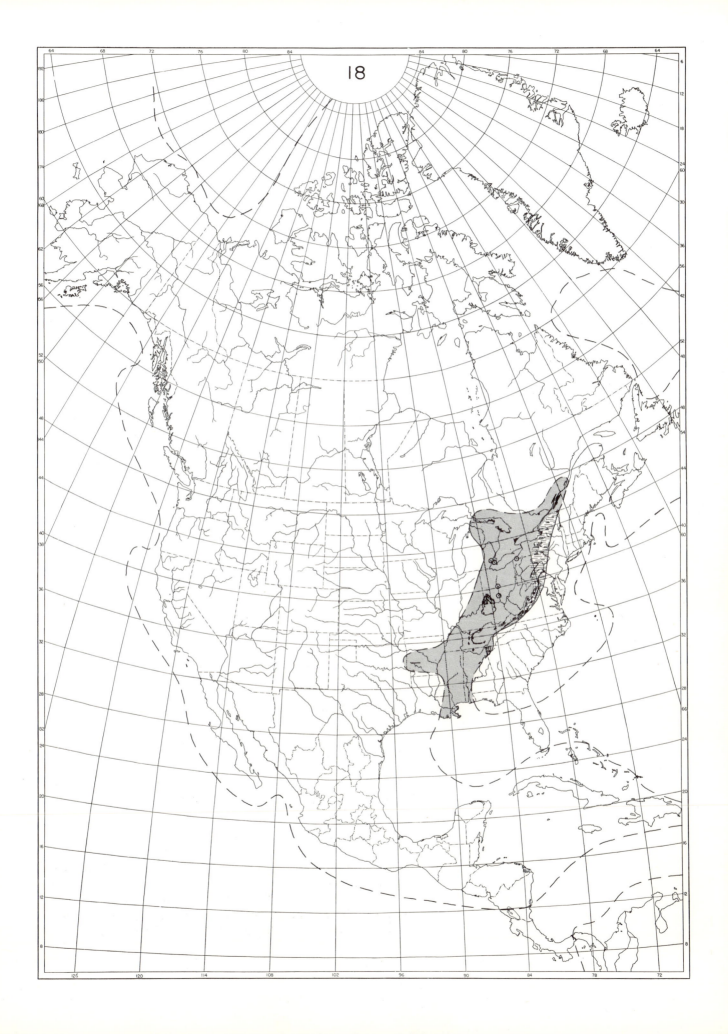

18

19

Upper Ordovician
Lower Richmondian (Arnheim)

STRATIGRAPHIC UNITS REPRESENTED

ALABAMA—Sequatchie fm. (part)

ARKANSAS—"Fernvale" ls.

GEORGIA—Sequatchie fm.

INDIANA—Arnheim ls.

KENTUCKY—Arnheim ls.

OHIO—Arnheim ls.

OKLAHOMA—"Fernvale" ls.

TENNESSEE—Arnheim ls. and Sequatchie fm. (part)

———

ANTICOSTI ISLAND—English Head fm.

Editor's note: This map shows a minimum extent of the *marine* early Richmondian. Almost certainly the lower part of the Juniata red beds of Virginia to Pennsylvania are of this age. Also the widespread Richmondian of the Arctic region and Canada (shown on Map 20) may be in part of early Richmondian age.

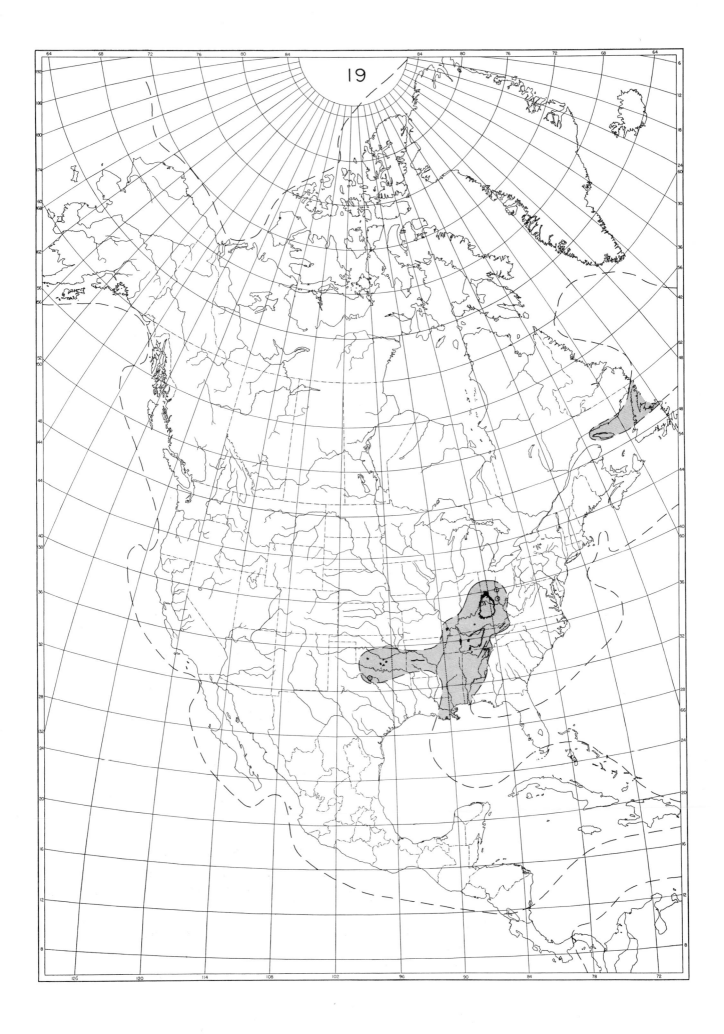

19

20

Upper Ordovician
Middle and Upper Richmondian

STRATIGRAPHIC UNITS REPRESENTED

ALABAMA—Sequatchie fm. (part)

ARKANSAS—Fernvale ls.

COLORADO—Fremont ls.

GEORGIA—Sequatchie fm. (part)

IDAHO—Saturday Mountain dol.

INDIANA—Waynesville sh. to Elkhorn ls. of Cincinnati arch

IOWA—Maquoketa fm.

KENTUCKY—Liberty fm., Saluda fm., Sequatchie fm. (part) and
    Waynesville sh. to Elkhorn ls. of Cincinnati arch

MARYLAND—Juniata ss. and Sequatchie fm. (part)

MICHIGAN—Bill's Creek beds to Big Hill ls.

MINNESOTA—Maquoketa fm.

MONTANA—Bighorn dol.

NEW MEXICO—Montoya dol.

NEW YORK—Queenston sh.

OHIO—Waynesville sh. to Elkhorn ls. of Cincinnati arch

OKLAHOMA—Fernvale ls., Polk Creek sh. of Ouachita Moun-
    tains, and Viola ls. (upper part) [may belong on Map 19]

PENNSYLVANIA—Juniata ss. and Sequatchie fm. (part)

SOUTH DAKOTA—Whitewood ls. of Black Hills

TENNESSEE—Fernvale ls. and Sequatchie fm. (part)

TEXAS, TRANS-PECOS—Maravillas chert and Montoya dol.

UTAH—Fish Haven dol. and Bighorn dol.

VIRGINIA—Juniata ss. and Sequatchie fm. (part)

WYOMING—Bighorn dol.

—————

ANTICOSTI ISLAND—Vaurial fm.

CANADIAN ROCKIES—Beaverfoot ls.

GASPÉ—Matapedia fm. and Whitehead ls.

HUDSON BAY—Shammattawa ls.

MANITOBA—Red River fm. and Stony Mountain fm.

ONTARIO—Kagawong ls. of Manitoulin Islands and Queenston
    sh.

QUEBEC—Liskeard ls. of Lake Timiskaming area

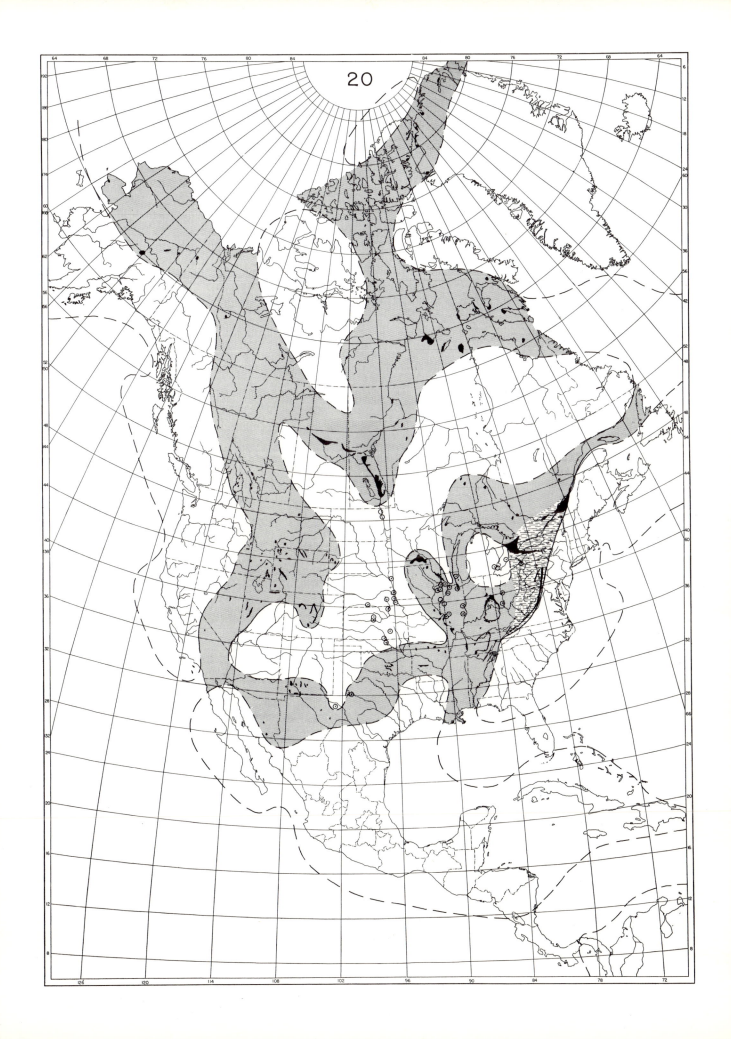

21

Lower Silurian

Lower Medinan

STRATIGRAPHIC UNITS REPRESENTED

ALABAMA—Red Mountain ss. (lower part)

ILLINOIS—Edgewood ls. and Girardeau ls.

KENTUCKY—Centerville sh.

MISSOURI—Edgewood ls. and Girardeau ls.

OHIO—Centerville sh.

———

ANTICOSTI ISLAND—Becsie River fm. and Gun River fm. (lower part)

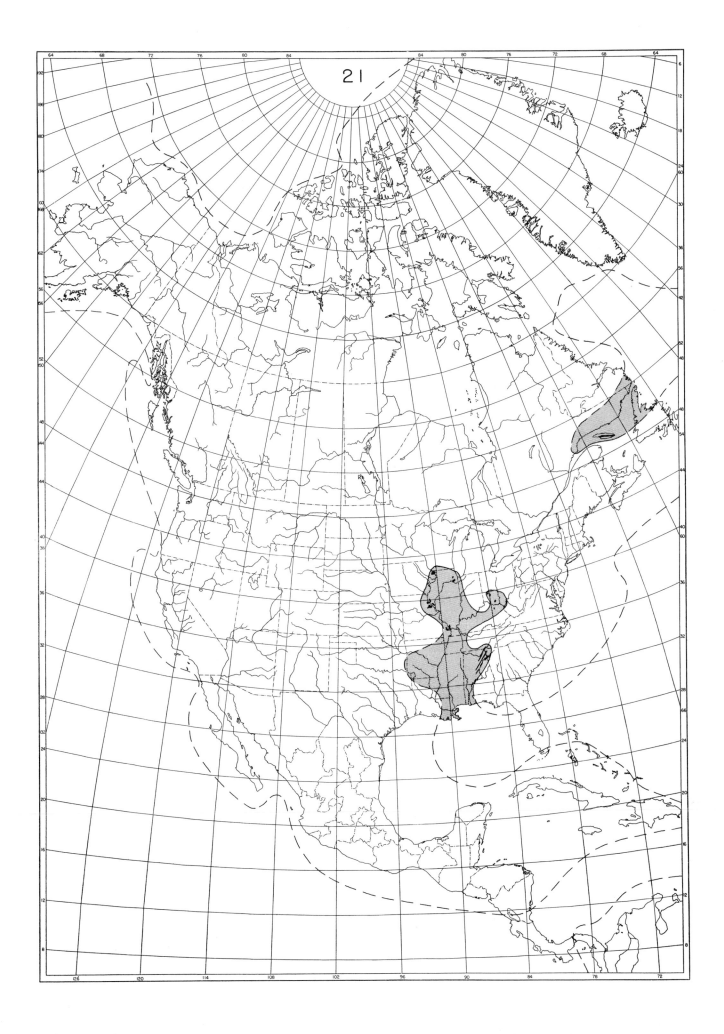

22

Lower Silurian
Middle Medinan

STRATIGRAPHIC UNITS REPRESENTED

ALABAMA—Clinch ss. (lower part) and Red Mountain fm. (part)

GEORGIA—Whiteoak ss.

IOWA—Waucoma ls.

MARYLAND—Clinch ss. (lower part) and Tuscarora ss. (part)

MICHIGAN—Manitoulin dol.

NEW YORK—Cabot Head sh., Medina ss. (lower part), and Shawangunk cgl. (lower part)

OHIO—Brassfield ls. of Ohio Valley

OKLAHOMA—Chimneyhill ls. of Arbuckle region

PENNSYLVANIA—Clinch ss. (lower part), Tuscarora ss. (part), and Shawangunk cgl. (lower part)

TENNESSEE—Clinch ss. (lower part), Whiteoak ss., and Red Mountain fm. (part)

VIRGINIA—Clinch ss. (lower part) and Tuscarora ss. (part)

WEST VIRGINIA—Tuscarora ss. (part)

———

ANTICOSTI ISLAND—Gun River fm. (lower part)

HUDSON BAY—Severn River ls.

MACKENZIE VALLEY—Franklin Mountain fm. (part)

MANITOBA—*Virgiana decussata* beds*

NOVA SCOTIA—Beechhill fm. (lower part)

ONTARIO—Cabot Head sh. and Manitoulin dol.

* *Editor's note:* Colin W. Stearn thinks these beds are basal Clinton *(Geol. Soc. Am., Bull.,* v. 64, p. 1477, 1953).

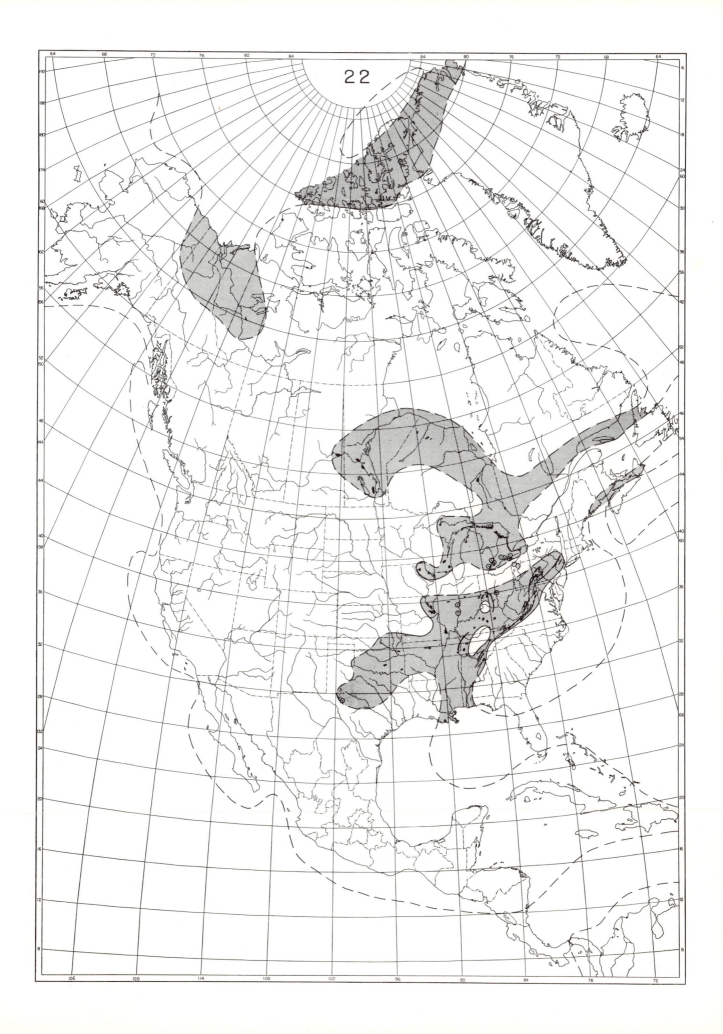

22

23

Lower Silurian
Upper Medinan

STRATIGRAPHIC UNITS REPRESENTED

ALABAMA—Clinch ss. (upper part) and Red Mountain ss. (mia dle part)

GEORGIA—Whiteoak ss. (upper part)

MARYLAND—Clinch ss. (upper part) and Tuscarora ss. (upper part)

MICHIGAN—Mayville ls.

NEW YORK—Cabot Head sh., Grisby ss., Medina ss. (upper part), and Shawangunk cgl. (part)

PENNSYLVANIA—Castanea ss., Clinch ss. (upper part), and Tuscarora ss. (upper part)

TENNESSEE—Clinch ss. (upper part) and Whiteoak ss. (upper part)

VIRGINIA—Clinch ss. (upper part) and Tuscarora ss. (upper part)

WISCONSIN—Mayville ls.

———

ANTICOSTI ISLAND—Gun River fm. (upper part)

MACKENZIE VALLEY—Franklin Mountain fm. (middle part)

NOVA SCOTIA—Beechhill fm. (upper part)

ONTARIO—Cabot Head sh., Grimsby ss., and Medina ss. (upper part)

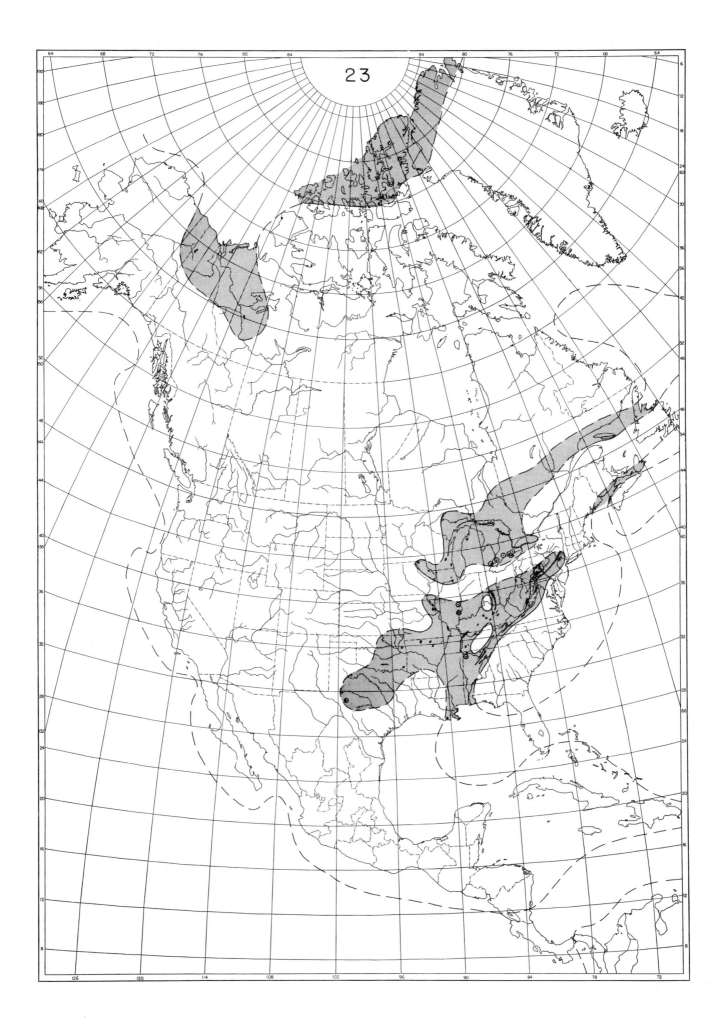

23

24

Middle Silurian
Lower Clinton

STRATIGRAPHIC UNITS REPRESENTED

ALABAMA—Red Mountain fm. (middle)

ARKANSAS—Blaylock ss.

KENTUCKY—Dayton ls., Lulbegrud cgl., Oldham ls., Plum Creek cgl., and Waco ls.

MARYLAND—Rose Hill sh. (lower part)

MICHIGAN—Burnt Bluff gr. (lower part) and St. Edmund dol. (low)

NEW YORK—Clinton gr. (lower part) and Shawangunk cgl. (upper part)

OHIO—Dayton ls., Lulbegrud cgl., Oldham ls., Plum Creek cgl., and Waco ls.

OKLAHOMA—Blaylock ss.

PENNSYLVANIA—Shawangunk cgl. (upper part)

————

ANTICOSTI ISLAND—Gun River fm. (high)

GASPÉ—Clemville fm.

GREENLAND—Cape Schuchert fm.

MACKENZIE VALLEY—Franklin Mountain ls. (upper)

NOVA SCOTIA—Ross Brook fm. (low)

ONTARIO—Burnt Bluff gr. (lower part) and St. Edmund dol. (low)

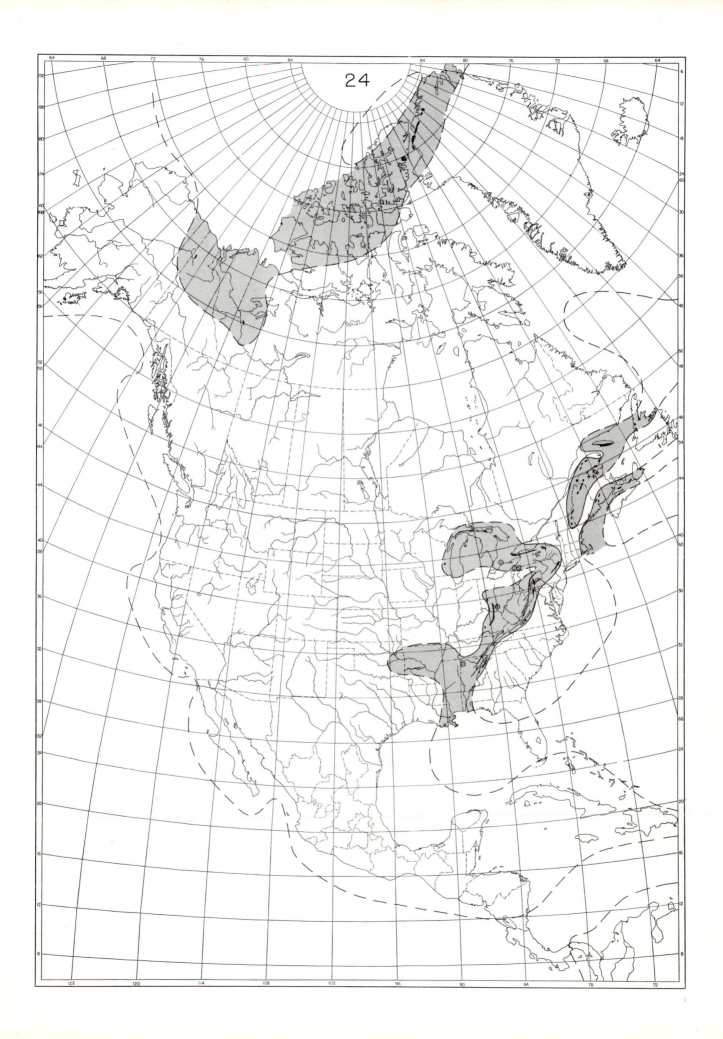

24

25

Middle Silurian
Upper Clinton

STRATIGRAPHIC UNITS REPRESENTED

ALABAMA—Red Mountain gr. (uppermost part)

ARKANSAS—St. Clair ls.

CALIFORNIA—Montgomery ls.

IDAHO—Trail Creek fm.

ILLINOIS—Hopkinton dol. (lower) and Rockdale dol.

INDIANA—Mississinewa sh., Osgood fm., and Rockdale dol.

IOWA—Hopkinton dol. (lower)

KENTUCKY—Bisher fm. (east-central)

MAINE—Quoddy fm.

MICHIGAN—Burnt Bluff fm. and Hendricks memb.

NEW YORK—Herkimer ss., Rochester sh., Shawangunk cgl. (upper)

OHIO—Bisher fm.

PENNSYLVANIA—Keefer ss. and Rochester sh.

TENNESSEE—Keefer ss., Rochester sh., and Sneedville ls. (lower)

————

ANTICOSTI ISLAND—Chicotte fm.

GASPÉ—Gascons fm. (lower) and La Vieille fm. (upper)

GREENLAND—Cape Tyson fm. (lower part) and Offley Island fm.

MACKENZIE VALLEY—Franklin Mountain ls.

NOVA SCOTIA—McAdam fm.

ONTARIO—Burnt Bluff fm., Hendricks memb.

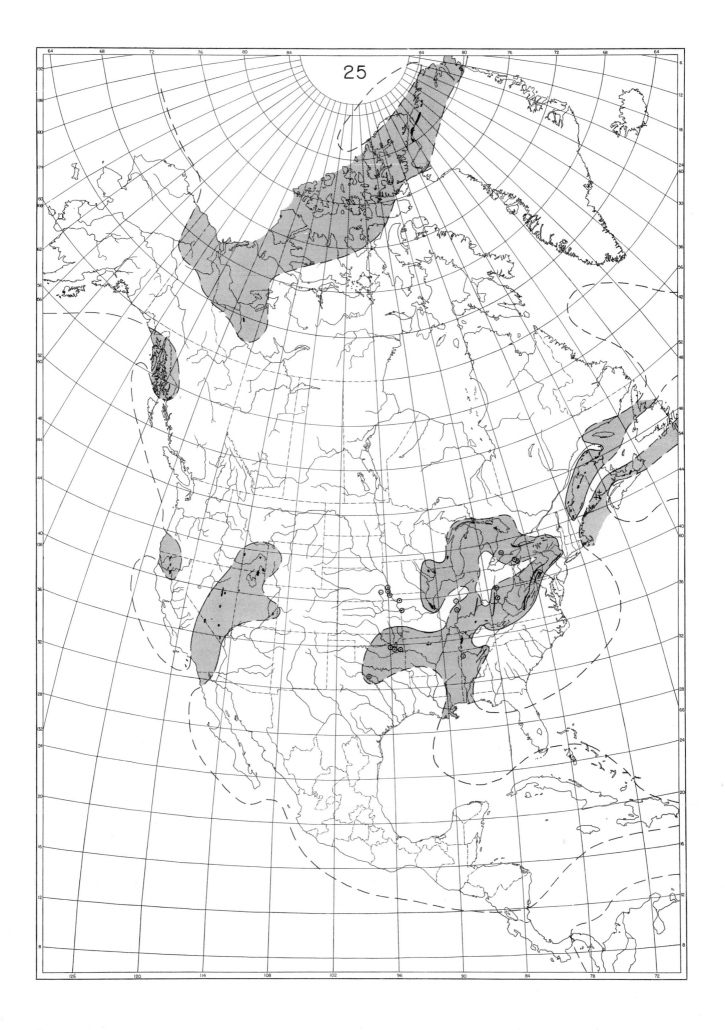

25

26

Middle Silurian
Lower Albamarle

STRATIGRAPHIC UNITS REPRESENTED

ARKANSAS—Lafferty ls.

CALIFORNIA—Montgomery ls.

IDAHO—Laketown dol.

ILLINOIS—Joliet dol. and Waukesha dol.

INDIANA—Liston Creek ls.

IOWA—Hopkinton dol. (upper) and Manistique dol. (upper)

KENTUCKY—Lilley fm.

MICHIGAN—Hopkinton dol. (upper) and Manistique dol. (upper)

MISSOURI—Bainbridge ls.

NEVADA—Lone Mountain ls.

NEW MEXICO—Fusselman ls. (lower)

OHIO—Lilley fm.

OKLAHOMA—Henryhouse sh.

TENNESSEE— Laurel ls. to Brownsport fm.

TEXAS—Fusselman ls. (lower)

————

GASPÉ—Bouleaux fm. and Gascons fm. (upper)

GREENLAND—Cape Tyson fm.

MACKENZIE VALLEY—Mount Kindle fm.

MANITOBA—Ekwan ls.

NOVA SCOTIA—Moydart fm. (lower)

ONTARIO—Ekwan ls., Hopkinton dol. (upper), and Manistique dol. (upper)

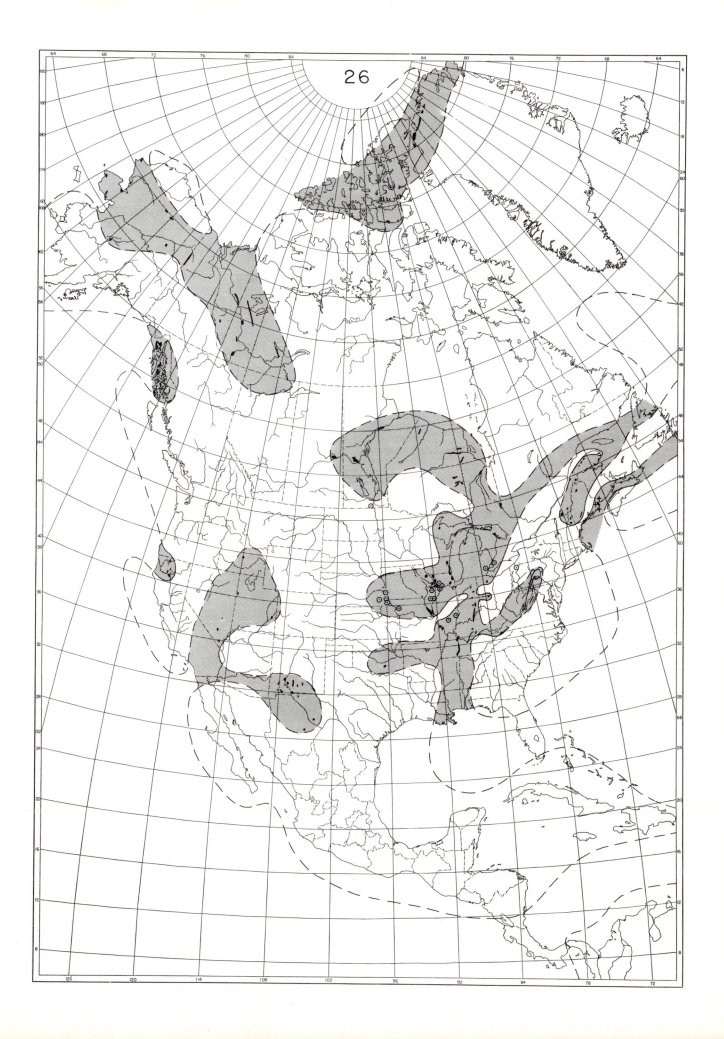

27

Middle Silurian
Middle Albamarle

STRATIGRAPHIC UNITS REPRESENTED

CALIFORNIA—Montgomery ls. (uppermost)

ILLINOIS—Port Byron dol. (lower part) and Racine dol.

IOWA—Gower dol.

MAINE—Dennys fm. and Moydart fm. (upper)

MICHIGAN—Engadine dol.

NEVADA—Lone Mountain ls. (upper)

NEW MEXICO—Fusselman ls. (upper)

NEW YORK—Eramosa dol., Gasport ls., and Suspension Bridge dol.

OHIO—Durbin gr.

TEXAS—Fusselman ls. (upper)

WISCONSIN—Huntington dol. (lower) and Racine dol.

———

GASPÉ—West Point fm.

GREENLAND—Cape Tyson fm.

MACKENZIE VALLEY—Mount Kindle fm. (upper)

MANITOBA—Attawapiskat ls. (lower)

NOVA SCOTIA—Dennys fm. and Moydart fm. (upper)

ONTARIO—Attawapiskat ls. (lower) and Engadine dol.

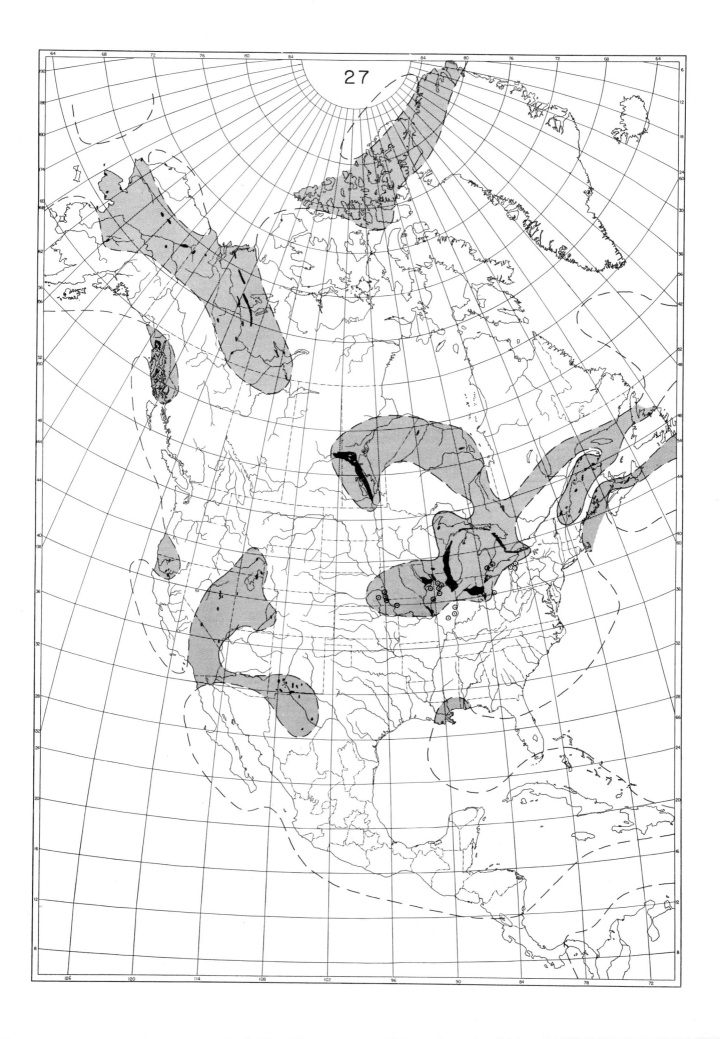

27

28

Middle Silurian
Upper Albamarle

STRATIGRAPHIC UNITS REPRESENTED

ILLINOIS—Port Byron dol.

INDIANA—Huntington dol. (upper)

IOWA—Bertram dol. and Port Byron dol.

MAINE—Edmunds fm. (lower)

NEW YORK—Guelph dol.

OHIO—Peebles dol.

———

GASPÉ—Indian Point fm.

GREENLAND—Cape Tyson fm.

HUDSON BAY—Attawapiskat ls. (upper)

MACKENZIE VALLEY—Mount Kindle fm. (upper)

MANITOBA—Attawapiskat ls. (upper)

NOVA SCOTIA—Moydart fm. (upper) and Stonehouse fm. (low)

ONTARIO—Guelph dol.

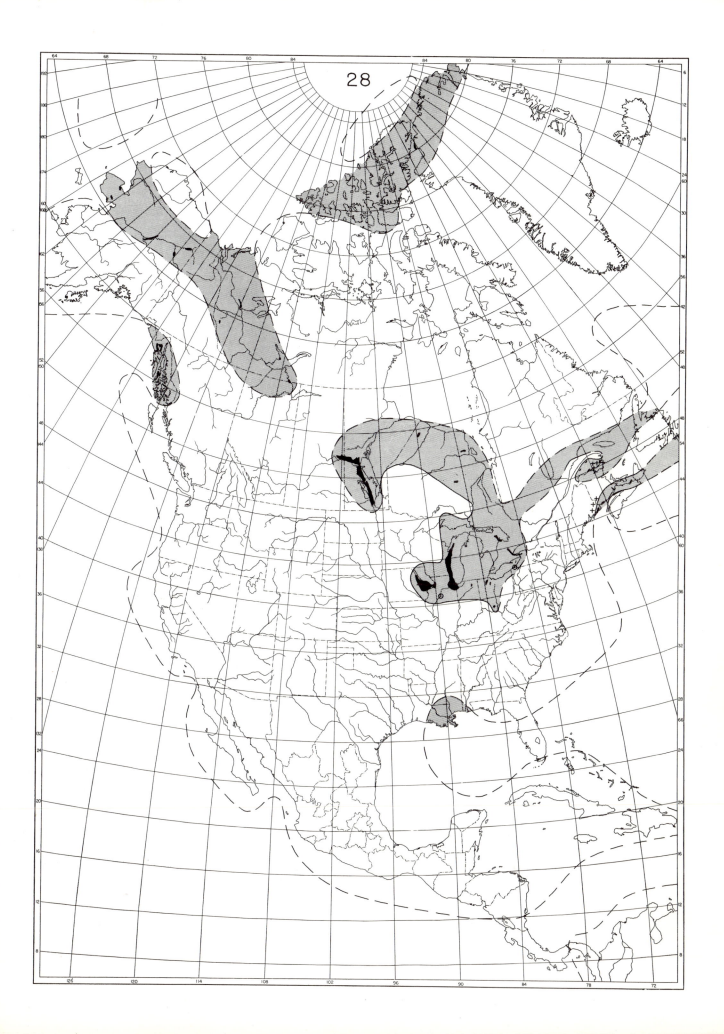

28

29

Upper Silurian
Lower Cayugan

STRATIGRAPHIC UNITS REPRESENTED

INDIANA—Kokomo dol.

MAINE—Edmunds fm. (upper) and Pembroke fm. (lower)

MARYLAND—Bloomsburg sh. (upper) and Wills Creek sh.

MICHIGAN—Greenfield dol., Put-in-Bay dol., and Tymochtee sh.

NEW JERSEY—Bossardville ls. and Poxino sh.

NEW YORK—Bertie ls., Bloomsburg sh. (upper), Bossardville ls.,
Salina gr., and Wills Creek sh.

OHIO—Greenfield dol., Put-in-Bay dol., and Tymochtee sh.

PENNSYLVANIA—Bloomsburg sh. (upper) and Wills Creek sh.

TENNESSEE—Bloomsburg sh. (upper) and Wills Creek sh.

VIRGINIA—Bloomsburg sh. (upper) and Wills Creek sh.

WEST VIRGINIA—Bloomsburg sh. (upper) and Wills Creek sh.

WISCONSIN—Waubakee ls. (east)

———

GREENLAND—Polaris Harbour fm. (lower)

MACKENZIE VALLEY—North Nahanna River dol. (lower)

NOVA SCOTIA—Stonehouse fm. (lower)

ONTARIO—Salina fm.

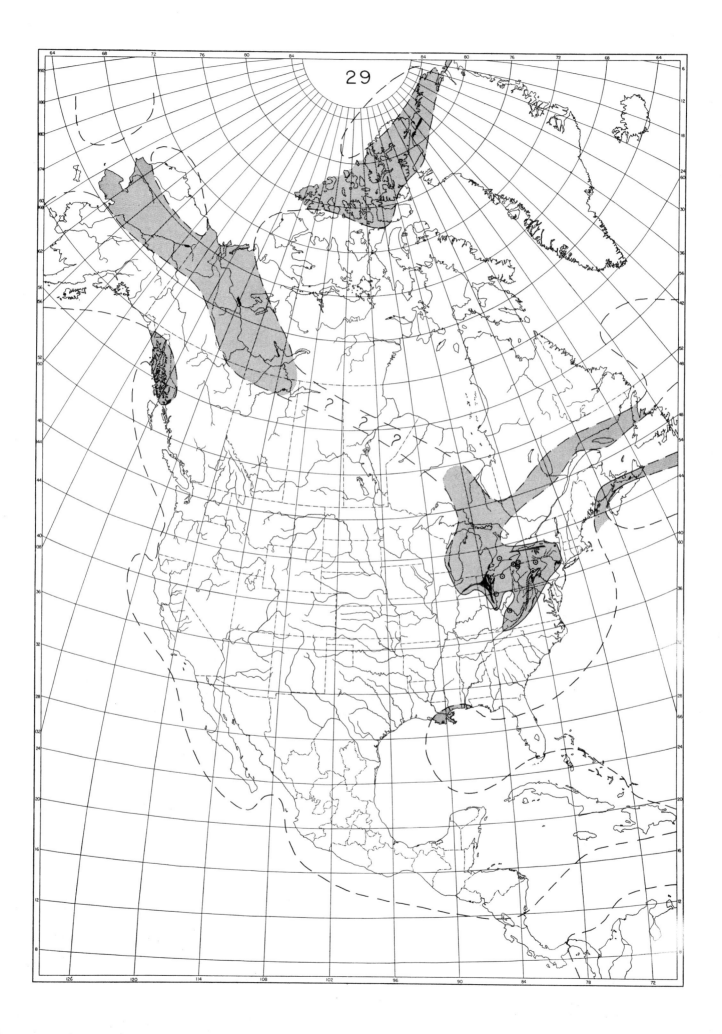

29

30

Upper Silurian

Upper Cayugan

STRATIGRAPHIC UNITS REPRESENTED

ARKANSAS—Missouri Mountain sl.

MAINE—Eastport fm. and Pembroke fm. (upper)

MARYLAND—Keyser ls.

NEW JERSEY—Decker Ferry ls. and Tonoloway ls.

NEW YORK—Cobbleskill ls., Decker Ferry ls., and Manlius ls.

PENNSYLVANIA—Keyser ls.

TENNESSEE—Sneedville ls. and Tonoloway ls.

VIRGINIA—Sneedville ls. and Tonoloway ls.

————

GREENLAND—Polaris Harbour fm.

NOVA SCOTIA—Stonehouse fm.

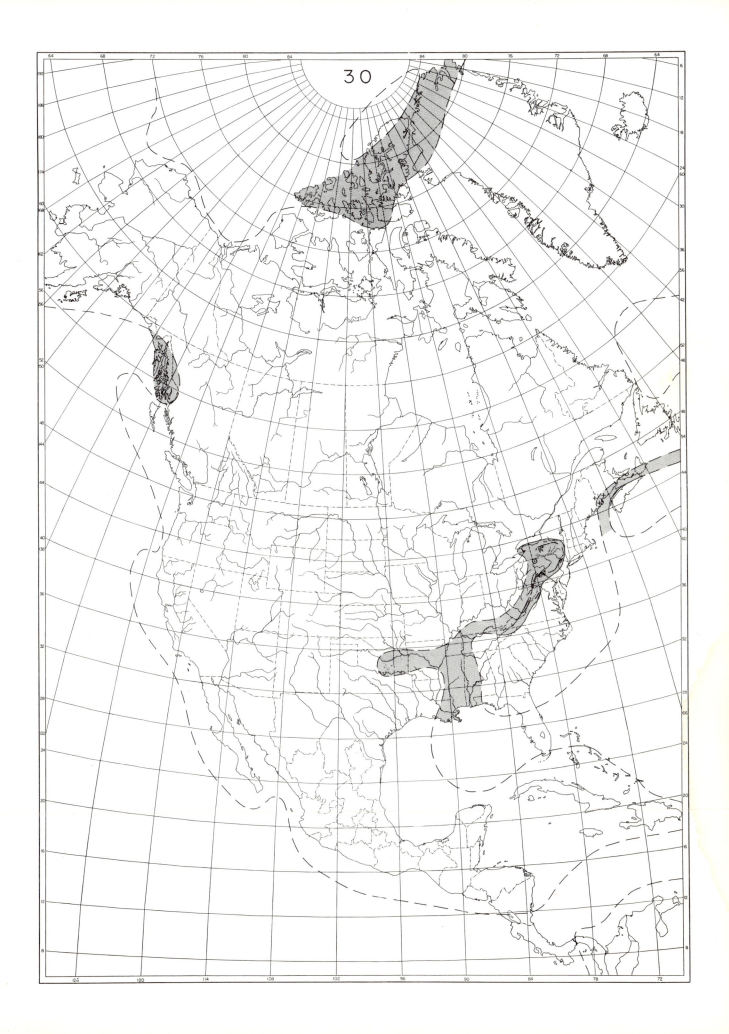

30

31

Lower Devonian
Helderbergian

STRATIGRAPHIC UNITS REPRESENTED

MAINE—Chapman ss. and Square Lake ls.

MISSOURI—Bailey ls.

NEW YORK—Becraft ls., Coeymans ls., and New Scotland ls.

OKLAHOMA—Bois d'Arch ls. and Haragan sh.

PENNSYLVANIA—Coeymans ls. and New Scotland ls.

TENNESSEE—Birdsong sh. and Olive Hill ls.

TEXAS—Pillar Bluff fm.

VIRGINIA—Coeymans ls. and New Scotland ls.

———

NEW BRUNSWICK—Dalhousie sh.

QUEBEC—Cape Barré fm., Cape Bon Ami ls., Mont Joli fm., and St. Albans sh.

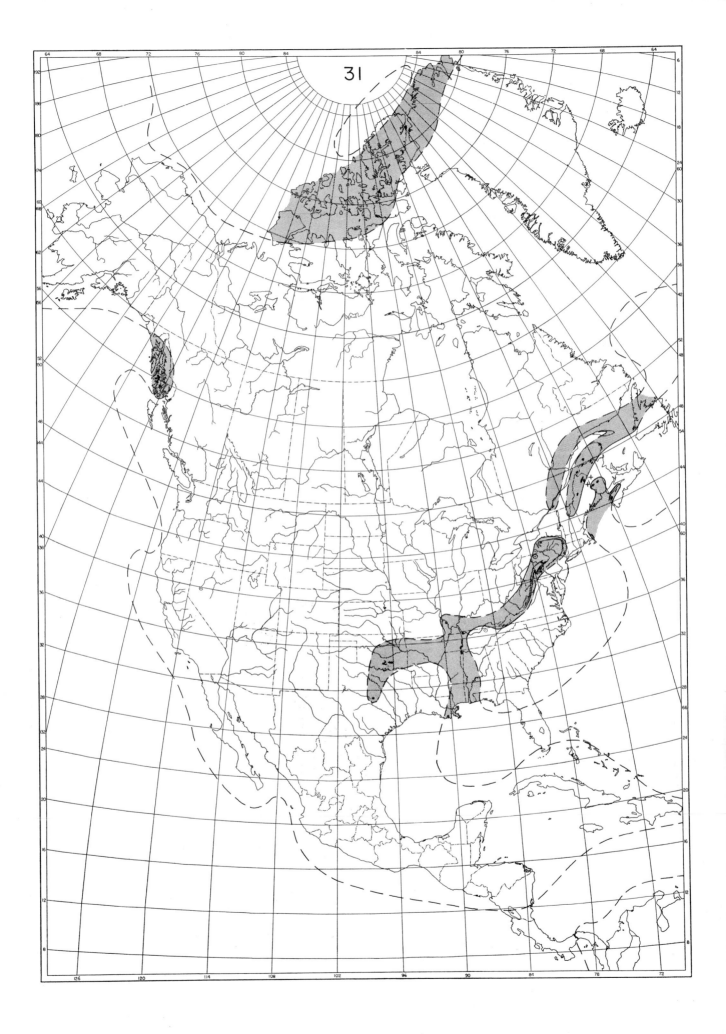

31

32

Lower Devonian
Oriskanian [Deerparkian]

STRATIGRAPHIC UNITS REPRESENTED

ARKANSAS—Arkansas novaculite (lower)

MAINE—Moose River ss.

MARYLAND—Ridgeley ss.

MICHIGAN—Garden Island fm.

MISSOURI—Backbone ls. and Little Saline ls.

NEW HAMPSHIRE—Littleton fm.

NEW YORK—Glenerie ls. and Oriskany ss.

OKLAHOMA—Frisco ls.

PENNSYLVANIA—Ridgeley ss.

TENNESSEE—Quall ls. and Harriman chert

VIRGINIA—Ridgeley ss.

WEST VIRGINIA—Ridgeley ss.

———

QUEBEC—Percé ls. and Grande Grève ls.

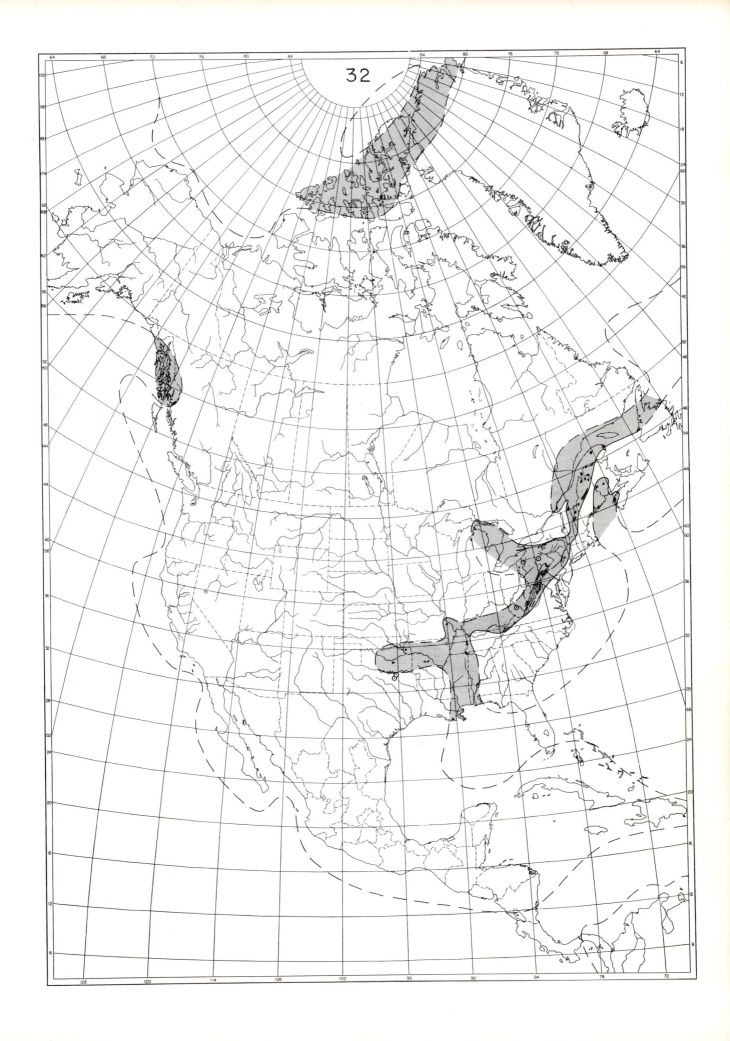

32

33

Middle Devonian
Lower Onondagan [Onesquethawian]

STRATIGRAPHIC UNITS REPRESENTED

ALABAMA—Frog Mountain ss.

ARKANSAS—Arkansas novaculite (lower part)

GEORGIA—Frog Mountain ss.

ILLINOIS—Clear Creek chert

MAINE—Moose River ss. (upper part)

MICHIGAN—Detroit River gr.

MISSOURI—Clear Creek chert

NEW YORK—Esopus sh., Onondaga ls. (basal part), and Schoharie sh.

PENNSYLVANIA—Esopus sh. and Schoharie sh.

TENNESSEE—Camden chert

TEXAS—Caballos novaculite

VIRGINIA—Huntersville chert, "Onondaga ls.," and Saltville chert

WEST VIRGINIA—Huntersville chert and Onondaga fm.

———

ONTARIO—Springvale fm.

QUEBEC—Causapscol fm., Gaspé ss., Heppel fm., and Fourmile Brook fm.

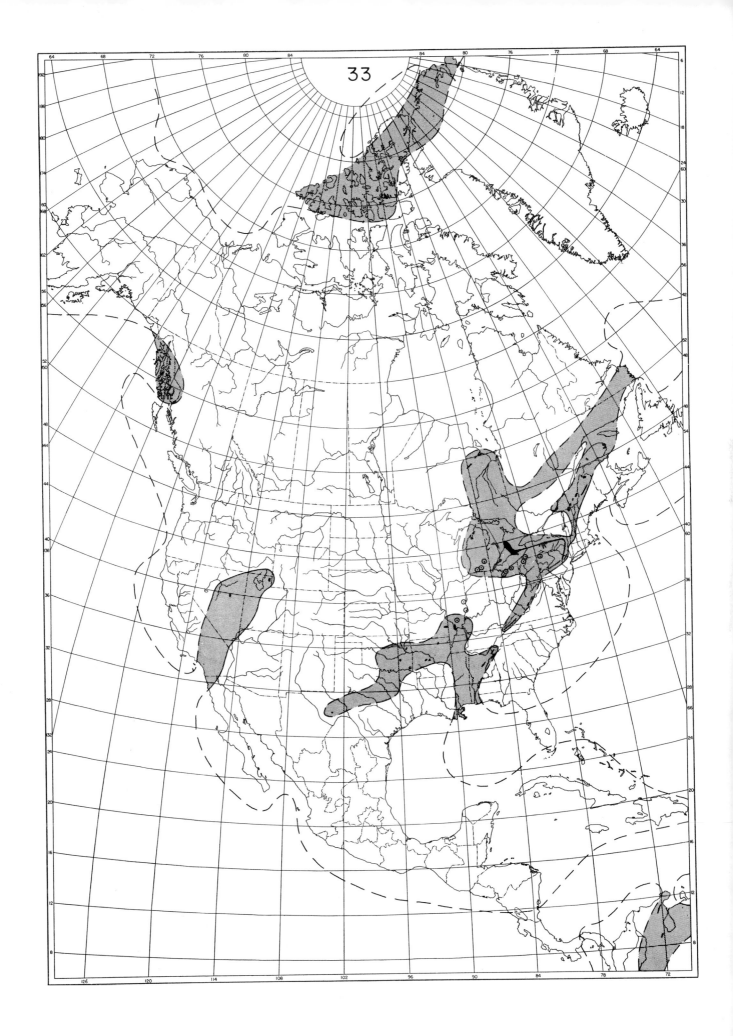

33

34

Middle Devonian

Upper Onondagan [Onesquethawian]

STRATIGRAPHIC UNITS REPRESENTED

ARKANSAS—Penters chert [probably lower Onesquethawian]

ILLINOIS—Grand Tower ls.

INDIANA—Pendleton ss.

KENTUCKY—Jeffersonville ls.

MASSACHUSETTS—Bernardston ls.

MICHIGAN—Bois Blanc ls. and Detroit River gr.

MISSOURI—Grand Tower ls.

NEVADA—Nevada ls. (part)

NEW YORK—Onondaga ls.

OHIO—Columbus ls.

OKLAHOMA—Pinetop chert

PENNSYLVANIA—Selinsgrove ls.

TENNESSEE—Pegram ls.

VIRGINIA—Needmore sh.

———

ONTARIO—Sextant fm. (James Bay region) and Onondaga ls.

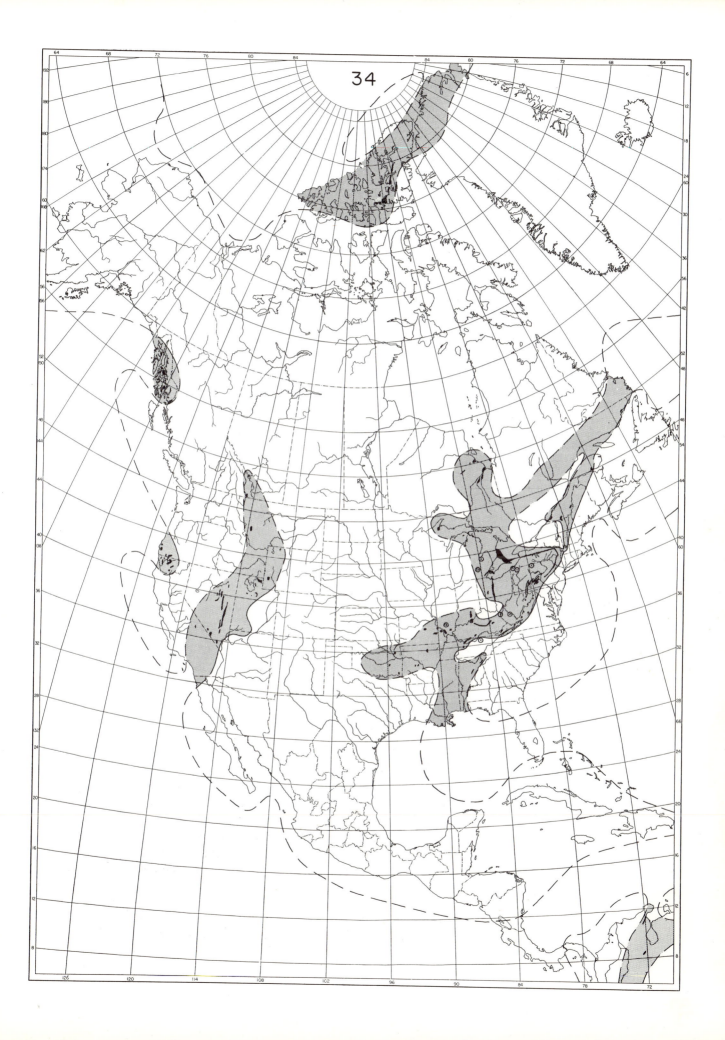

34

35

Middle Devonian
Marcellus

STRATIGRAPHIC UNITS REPRESENTED

ALABAMA—Ragland ss.

CALIFORNIA—Kennett fm.

ILLINOIS—Grand Tower ls. (part)

INDIANA—Speeds ls.

KENTUCKY—Boyle ls. (part)

MARYLAND—Marcellus sh.

MICHIGAN—Dundee ls. and Rogers City ls.

MISSOURI—Grand Tower ls. (part)

NEVADA—Guilmette fm., Nevada ls. (lower part), and Simonson dol.

NEW YORK—Marcellus stage

OHIO—Delaware ls.

PENNSYLVANIA—Marcellus sh.

TENNESSEE—Pegram ls. (upper part)

VIRGINIA—Marcellus sh.

———

ALBERTA—Flume ls.

MACKENZIE VALLEY—Hare Indian River sh., Pine Point ls., Presque Isle dol., and Ramparts ls.

MANITOBA—Elm Point ls. and Winnipegosan dol.

ONTARIO—Abitibi River ls. and Delaware ls.

QUEBEC—Gaspé ss.

Editor's note: The Rogers City limestone of the Michigan Basin shows faunal connection with the Winnipegosan dolomite of Manitoba. Possible connection is suggested by the broken lines.

The seaway crossing Iowa and northeast Missouri, based on the Cedar Valley limestone in Iowa and the Snyder Creek shale in Missouri, probably should be deleted here. See Map 37.

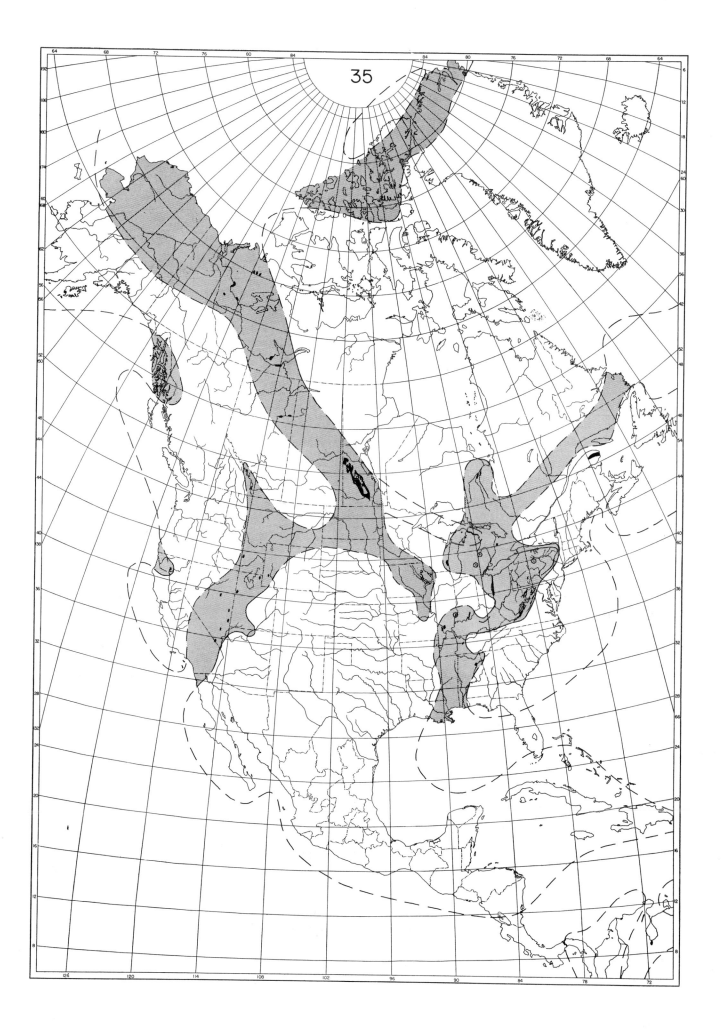

36

Middle Devonian
Skaneateles, Ludlowville, and Moscow

STRATIGRAPHIC UNITS REPRESENTED

ARKANSAS—Clifty fm.

ILLINOIS—Lingle ls., Misenheimer sh., and St. Laurent ls.

INDIANA—Logansport ls. and Sellersburg ls. (upper part)

KENTUCKY—Sellersburg ls. (upper part)

MICHIGAN—Traverse gr.

NEVADA—Devils Gate fm. (part) [may be Upper Devonian]

NEW YORK—Ludlow stage, Moscow stage, and Skaneateles stage

OHIO —Plum Creek sh. and Silica sh. (upper part)

PENNSYLVANIA—Mahantanga fm. and Skaneateles fm.

UTAH—Guilmette ls. (part)

————

MACKENZIE VALLEY—[Large area of outcrop in upper Mackenzie Valley country includes all of Middle and Upper Devonian formations and probably needs to be much restricted.]

ONTARIO—Arkona sh.; Ipperwash ls.; Hungry Hollow ls.; Petrolia sh.; Widder sh.; and, in James Bay region, Williams Island ls.

Editor's note: New England—Igneous rocks of the Oliverian magma series indicated by x's.

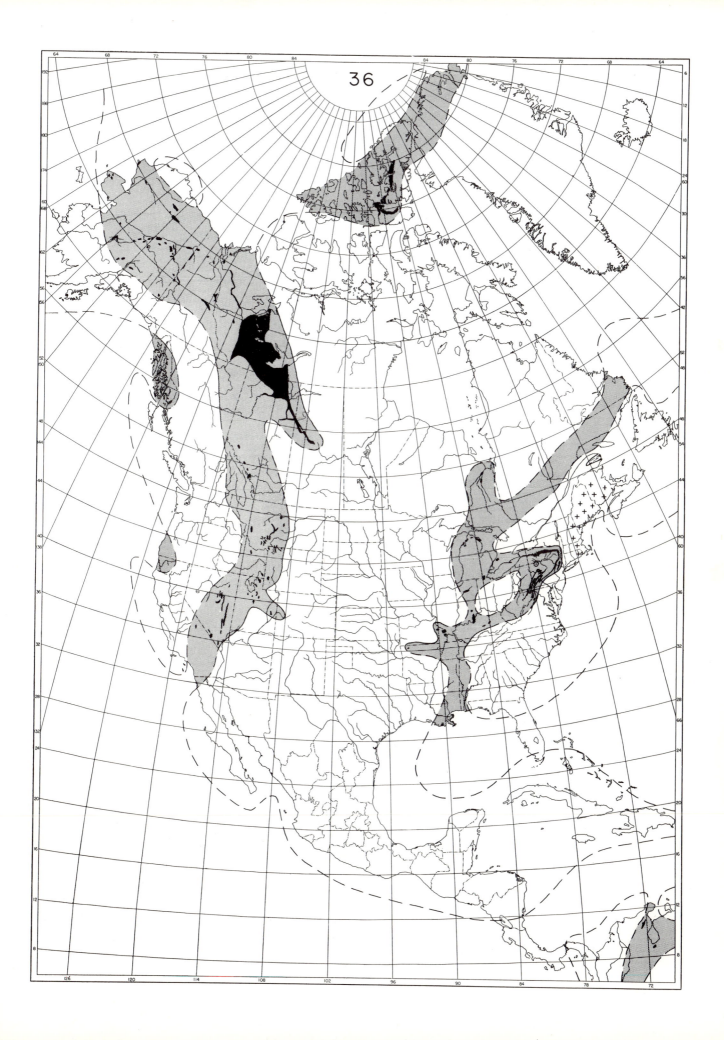

36

37

Lowest Upper Devonian
Geneseean

STRATIGRAPHIC UNITS REPRESENTED

ARKANSAS—"Chattanooga" sh.

IDAHO—Jefferson ls. (basal part)

ILLINOIS—Alto fm.

INDIANA—Delphi sh. (basal part) and New Albany sh. (part)

KENTUCKY—New Albany sh. (part)

MICHIGAN—Huron sh. (basal part), Petoskey ls. (part), and Squaw Bay ls.

MISSOURI—Alto fm. and Snyder Creek sh.

MONTANA—Jefferson ls. (basal part)

NEVADA—Muddy Peak ls. (lower part), Silverhorn dol. (part), and Sultan ls. (lower part)

NEW YORK—Geneseo sh. to Genundewa ls., Sherburne ss., and West River sh.

OHIO—Huron sh. (basal part)

PENNSYLVANIA—Harrell fm. and Trimmers Rock fm.

UTAH—Guilmette ls. (part)

VIRGINIA—Genesee sh. and Millboro sh. (upper part)

WEST VIRGINIA—Genesee sh. and Woodmont sh. (lower part)

WYOMING—Jefferson ls. (basal part)

———

ALBERTA—Ghost River fm.

BRITISH COLUMBIA—Mount Forster sh.

MACKENZIE VALLEY—Beavertail ls. and Slave Point ls.

ONTARIO—Huron sh. (lower part) and Long Rapids sh. (James Bay area)

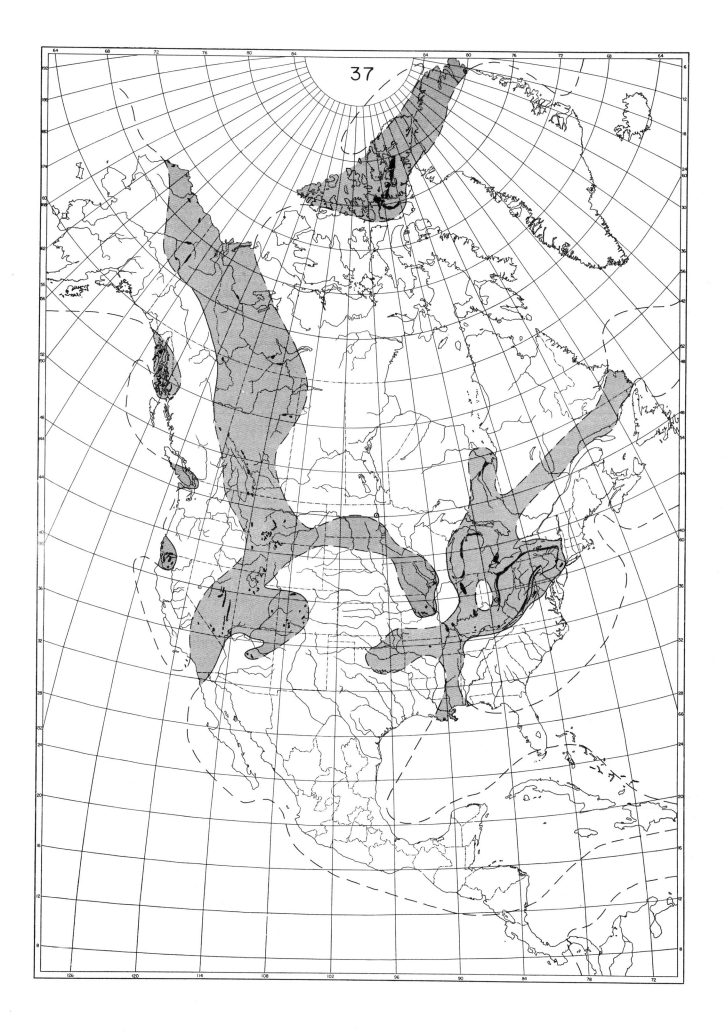

37

38

Middle and High Upper Devonian

STRATIGRAPHIC UNITS REPRESENTED

ARIZONA—Ouray ls., Martin sh., and Jerome fm.

COLORADO—Chaffee fm. and Elbert fm.

IDAHO—Jefferson ls. (part) and Threeforks ls.

INDIANA—Delphi sh. and New Albany sh. (part)

IOWA—Hackberry sh. and Shell Rock ls.

KENTUCKY—New Albany sh.

MICHIGAN—Antrim sh. and Huron sh.

MONTANA—Darby fm. and Jefferson ls. (part)

NEVADA—Devils Gate ls.

NEW MEXICO—Percha sh. and Sly Gap fm.

NEW YORK—Canadaway gr., Chemung gr., Conneaut gr., and
    Naples gr.

OHIO—Chagrin sh., Huron sh., and Ohio sh.

PENNSYLVANIA—Brallier sh., "Catskill" red beds, Chemung gr.,
    and Trimmers Rock ss.

UTAH—Mowitza sh.

VIRGINIA—Brailler sh. and "Chemung" ss.

WEST VIRGINIA—Brailler sh. and "Chemung" ss.

WYOMING—Darby fm. and Jefferson ls. (part)

———

ALBERTA—Boule ls., Exshaw sh., Minnewanka ls., and Perdrix
    sh.

MACKENZIE VALLEY—Carcajou Mountain sh., Forked Creek sh.,
    Hay River fm., and Simpson sh.

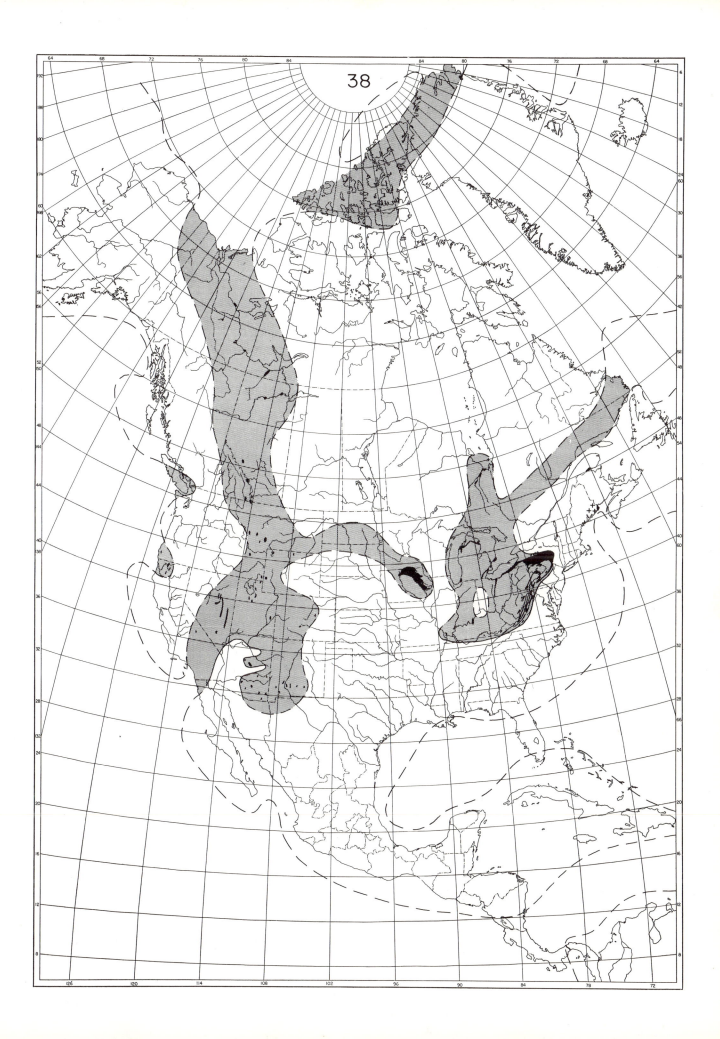

39

Lower Mississippian
Basal Kinderhookian (Fabius gr.)

STRATIGRAPHIC UNITS REPRESENTED

ALABAMA—Chattanooga sh.

ARKANSAS—Arkansas novaculite (part), Chattanooga sh., and Sylamore ss.

GEORGIA—Chattanooga sh.

ILLINOIS—Grassy Creek sh., Hardin ss., Louisiana ls., New Albany sh. (middle part), and Saverton sh.

KENTUCKY—Chattanooga sh.

MICHIGAN—Antrim sh. (upper part)

MISSOURI—Chattanooga sh. and Sylamore ss.

OHIO—Cleveland sh. and Ohio sh. (upper part)

OKLAHOMA—Chattanooga sh., Sylamore ss., and Woodford chert (part)

PENNSYLVANIA—Cussewago gr.

TENNESSEE—Chattanooga sh.

VIRGINIA—Chattanooga sh.

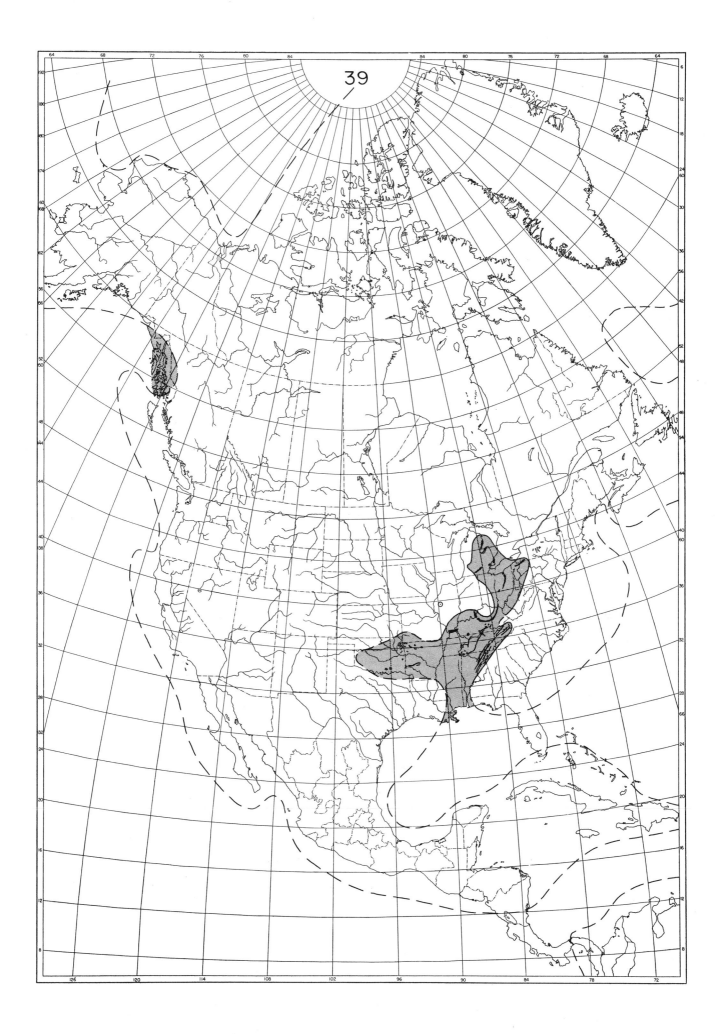

39

40

Lower Mississippian
Middle Kinderhookian (Easley gr., lower part)

STRATIGRAPHIC UNITS REPRESENTED

ALABAMA—Chattanooga sh. (upper part)

ILLINOIS—Bushberg ss., Glen Park ls., and Hannibal sh.

IOWA—Maple Mill sh. (upper part)

KENTUCKY—Bedford sh., Berea ss., and Sunbury sh.

MICHIGAN—Bedford sh., Berea ss., and Sunbury sh.

MISSOURI—Bushberg ss.

OHIO—Bedford sh., Berea ss., Cuyahoga gr. (lower part), and Sunbury sh.

PENNSYLVANIA—Corry ss., Cuyahoga gr. (lower part), and Pocono ss. (part)

VIRGINIA—Big Stone Gap sh. and Olinger sh.

WEST VIRGINIA—Berea ss. and Sunbury sh.

———

NEW BRUNSWICK—Memramcook fm.

NOVA SCOTIA—Horton gr. (lower part)

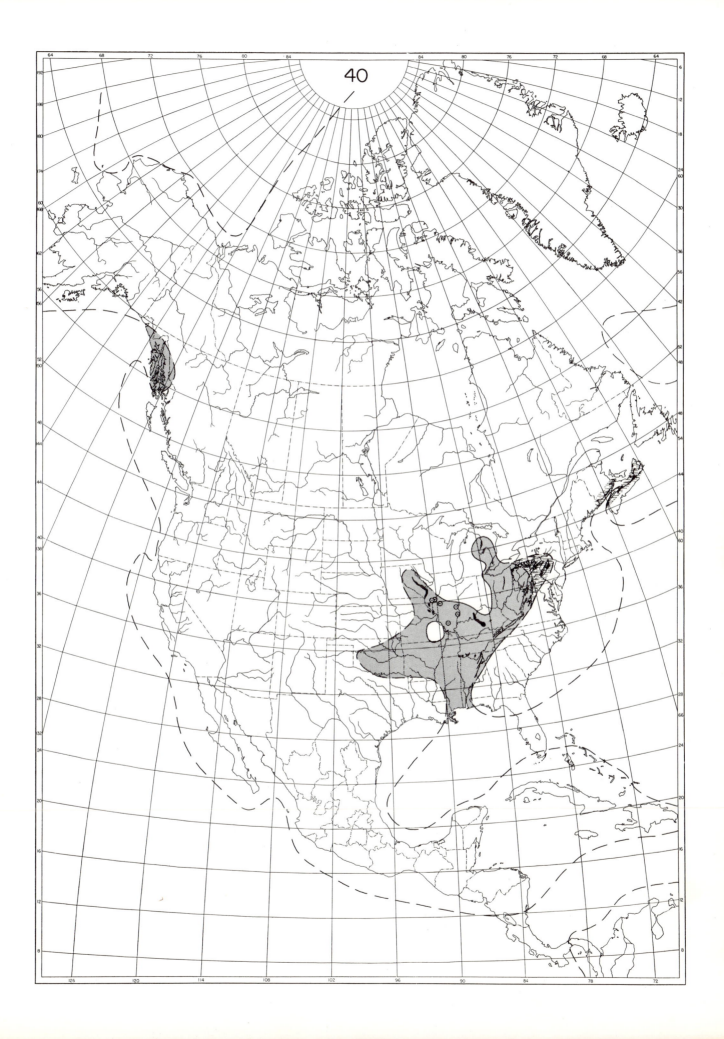

40

41

Lower Mississippian
Upper Kinderhookian

STRATIGRAPHIC UNITS REPRESENTED

ARIZONA—Escabrosa ls. (part) and Redwall ls. (part)

COLORADO—Leadville ls. (lower part)

IDAHO—Madison ls. (part) and Milligen fm.

IOWA—Gilmore City ls. and Hampton fm.

KENTUCKY—New Providence sh. (basal part)

MARYLAND—Pocono ss. (part)

MICHIGAN—Coldwater sh. (part) and Marshall ss.

MISSOURI—Chouteau ls. and Sedalia ls.

MONTANA—Madison ls. (part)

NEVADA—Bristol Pass ls. (part), Dawn ls. (upper part), Pilot sh. (part), and Rogers Spring ls. (part)

NEW MEXICO—Caballero fm.

OHIO—Cuyahoga gr. (upper part)

PENNSYLVANIA—Pocono ss. (part)

SOUTH DAKOTA—Pahasapa ls. (lower part)

TENNESSEE—New Providence sh. (basal part)

UTAH—Gardner dol. (part) and Madison ls. (part)

VIRGINIA—Price fm. (lower part)

WEST VIRGINIA—Pocono ss. (part)

WYOMING—Guernsey ls. (part) and Madison ls. (part)

———

ALBERTA—Banff ls. (part)

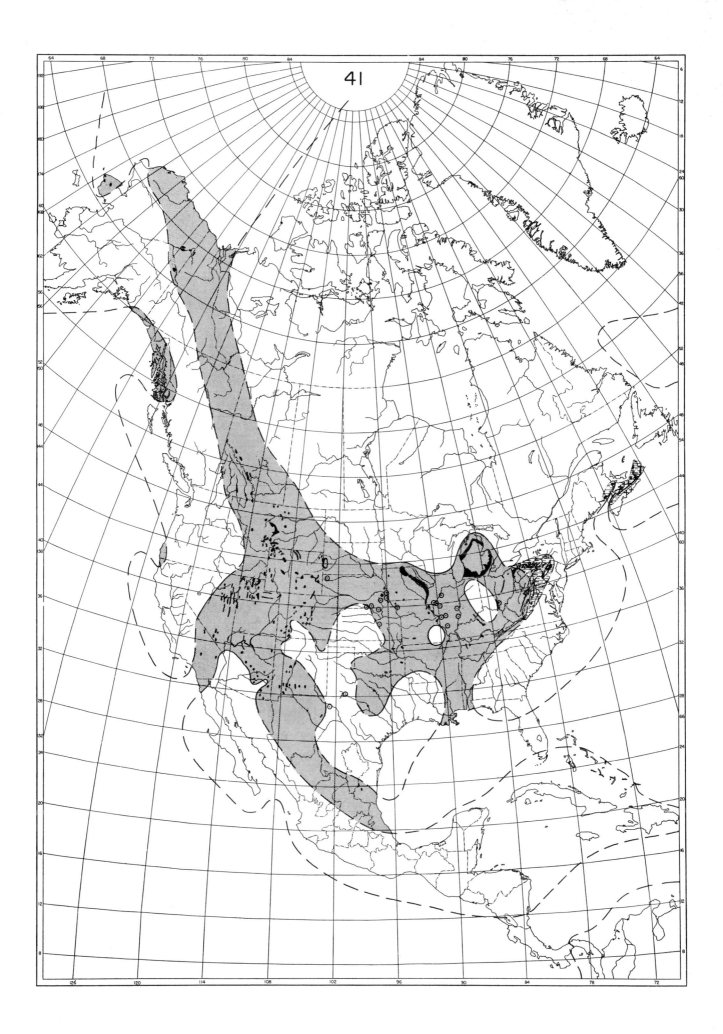

41

42

Middle Mississippian
Lower Osagean

STRATIGRAPHIC UNITS REPRESENTED

ALABAMA—Fort Payne chert (lower part)

ARKANSAS—Boone chert (lower part)

CALIFORNIA—Monte Cristo ls. (part)

COLORADO—Leadville ls. (part) and Madison ls. (part)

ILLINOIS—Burlington ls. and Fern Glen fm.

INDIANA—New Providence sh. (upper part)

IOWA—Burlington ls.

KENTUCKY—New Providence sh. (upper part)

MARYLAND—Pocono ss. (upper part)

MICHIGAN—Napoleon ss.

MISSOURI—Boone chert (lower part), Reeds Spring ls., and St. Joe ls.

MONTANA—Madison ls. (part)

NEVADA—Anchor ls., Joana ls. (lower part), Peers Spring fm. (lower part), Rogers Spring ls. (part)

NEW MEXICO—Lake Valley ls.

OHIO—Cuyahoga fm. (upper part) and Logan fm.

PENNSYLVANIA—Pocono gr. (middle part) and Shenango fm.

SOUTH DAKOTA—Pahasapa ls. (part)

TENNESSEE—Fort Payne chert (lower part) and New Providence sh. (upper part)

UTAH—Madison ls. (part) and Redwall ls. (part)

VIRGINIA—Price fm. (upper part)

WEST VIRGINIA—Logan ss.

WYOMING—Guernsey ls. (part) and Madison ls. (part)

———

ALBERTA—Banff sh. (upper part)

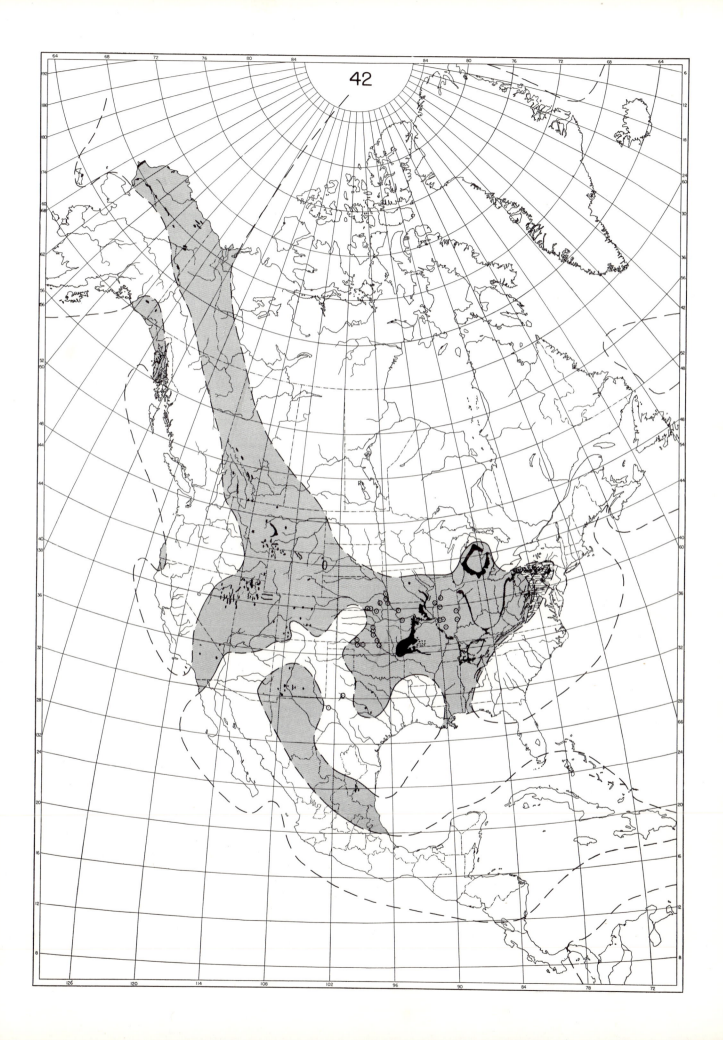

43

Middle Mississippian
Upper Osagean

STRATIGRAPHIC UNITS REPRESENTED

ALABAMA—Fort Payne chert (upper part)

ARKANSAS—Boone chert (upper part)

GEORGIA—Fort Payne chert (upper part)

ILLINOIS—Keokuk ls.

INDIANA—Borden gr. (upper part)

IOWA—Keokuk ls.

KENTUCKY—Brodhead fm., Floyds Knob fm., and Muldrough fm.

MARYLAND—Maccrady fm. (upper part)

MICHIGAN—Michigan fm. (middle part)

MISSOURI—Boone chert (upper part)

OKLAHOMA—Boone chert (upper part)

PENNSYLVANIA—Pocono gr. (upper part)

TENNESSEE—Fort Payne chert (upper part) and Grainger sh.

WEST VIRGINIA—Maccrady gr. (upper part)

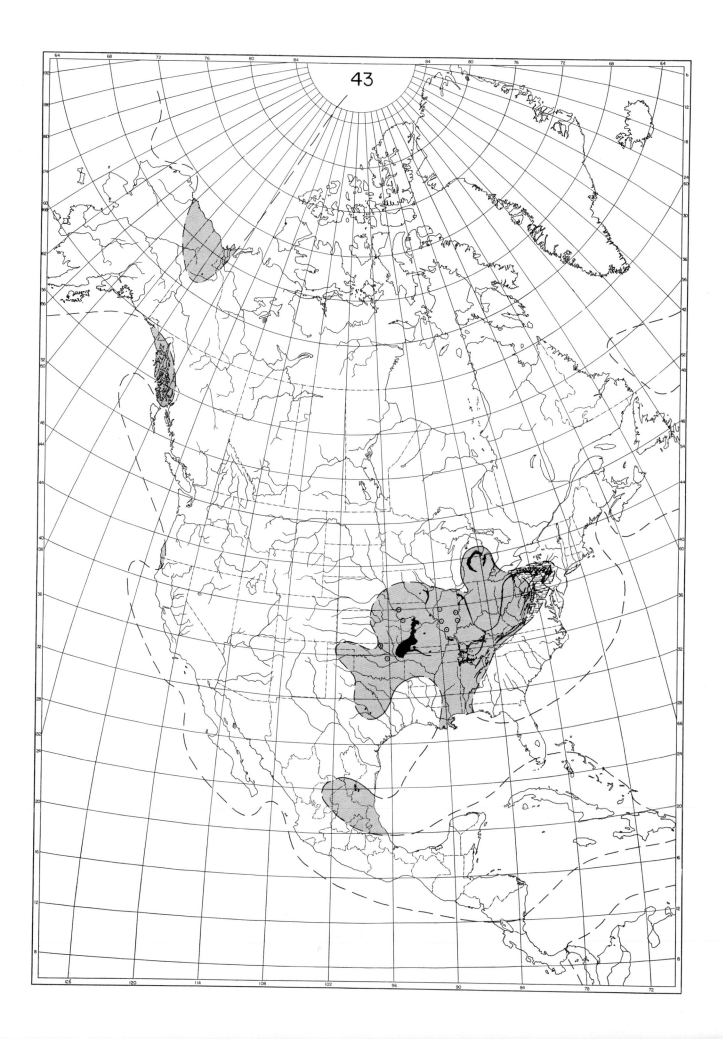

43

44

Middle Mississippian
Lower Meramecian

STRATIGRAPHIC UNITS REPRESENTED

ALABAMA—Warsaw ls.

GEORGIA—St. Louis ls. and Warsaw ls.

IDAHO—Brazer fm. (lower part) and Milligen fm. (part)

ILLINOIS—St. Louis ls., Salem ls., and Warsaw ls.

IOWA—St. Louis ls., Spergen ls., and Warsaw ls.

MICHIGAN—Bayport ls. and Michigan fm. (upper part)

MISSOURI—St. Louis ls., Spergen ls., and Warsaw ls.

NEVADA—Arrowhead ls., Bluepoint ls., Scotty Wash qtzite., White Pine sh., and Yellowpine ls.

UTAH—Deseret ls., Pine Canyon sh., and Redwall ls. (part)

VIRGINIA—Hillsdale ls. and Little Valley ls.

WEST VIRGINIA—Hillsdale ls. and Maccrady gr. (upper part)

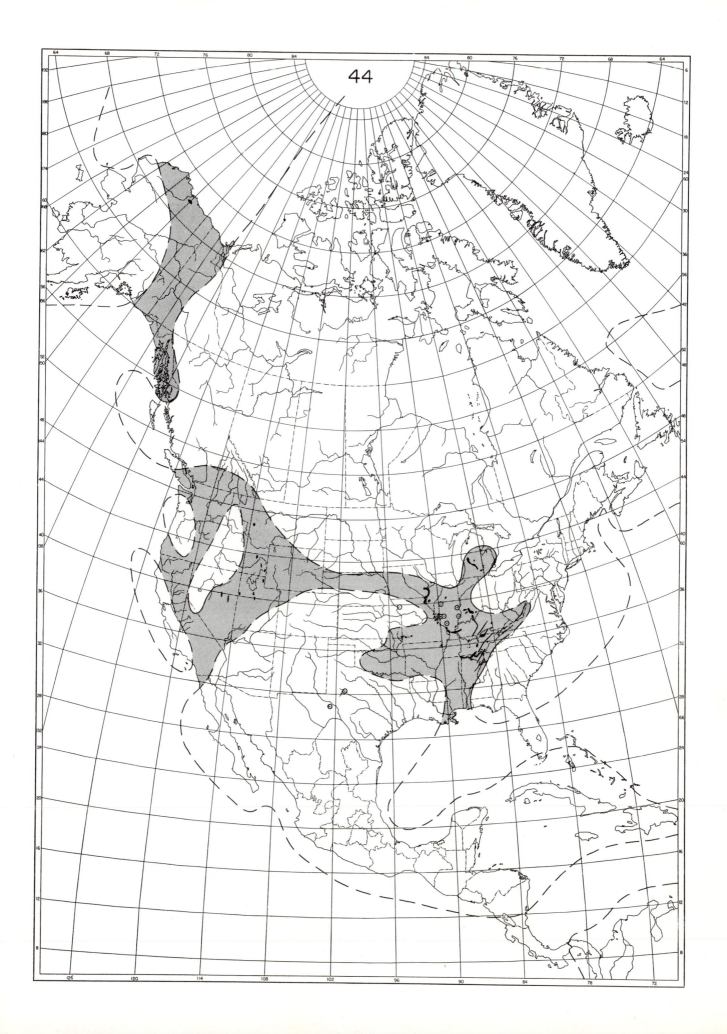

44

45

Middle Mississippian
Upper Meramecian

STRATIGRAPHIC UNITS REPRESENTED

ALABAMA—Ste. Genevieve ls.

CALIFORNIA—Baird sh. (part) and Relief qtzite. (part)

IDAHO—Brazer ls. (part) and Milligen fm. (part)

ILLINOIS—Ste. Genevieve ls.

INDIANA—Ste. Genevieve ls.

IOWA—Pella ls. and Ste. Genevieve ls.

KENTUCKY—Ste. Genevieve ls.

MARYLAND—Loyalhanna ls.

MISSOURI—Ste. Genevieve ls.

MONTANA—Kibbey fm. and Monitor Mountain ls. (upper part)

NEVADA—Chainman sh. (part), Bluepoint ls. (upper part), Scotty Wash qtzite. (upper part), and White Pine sh. (part)

OHIO—Maxville ls.

OREGON—Coffee Creek fm. (part)

PENNSYLVANIA—Loyalhanna ls.

TENNESSEE—Ste. Genevieve ls.

UTAH—Humbug ls.

WEST VIRGINIA—Greenbrier gr. (middle part)

———

ALASKA—Calico Bluff fm. (part) and Lisburne ls. (part)

ALBERTA—Rundle ls. (upper part)

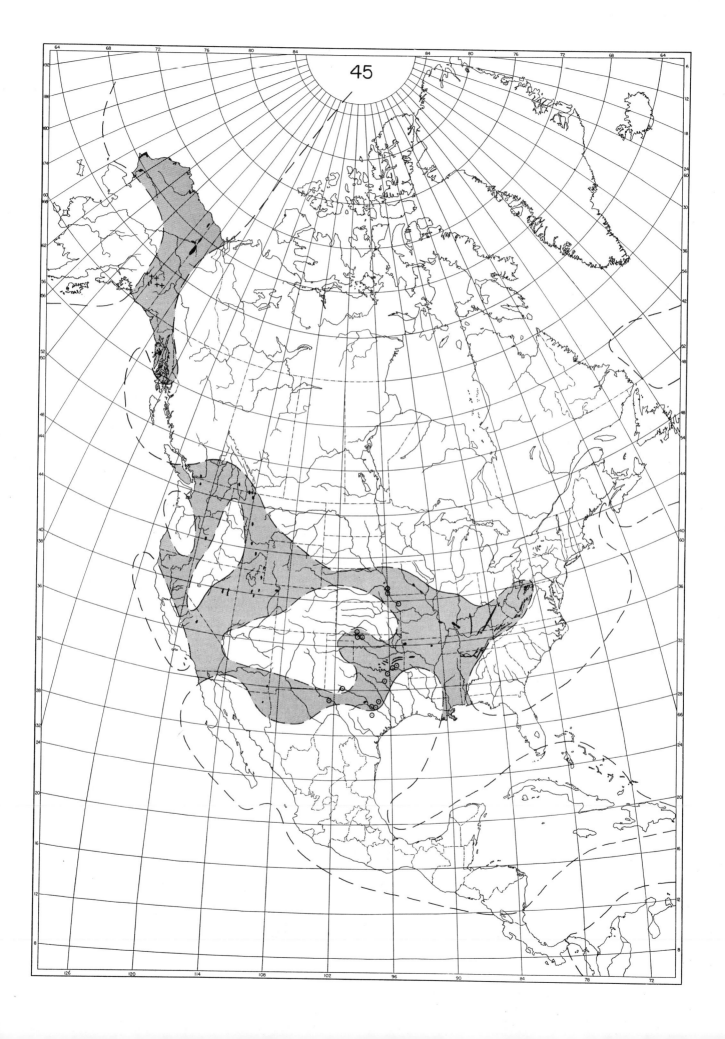

45

46

Upper Mississippian
Lower Chesterian

STRATIGRAPHIC UNITS REPRESENTED

ALABAMA—Bethel ss. and Gasper ls. (lower part)

ARIZONA—Paradise fm. (upper part)

ARKANSAS—Batesville ss.

IDAHO—Brazer fm. (part) and Milligen fm. (part)

ILLINOIS—Benoist ss., Paint Creek fm., and Renault fm.

INDIANA—Paint Creek fm., Renault fm., and Sample ss.

KENTUCKY—Gasper ls. and Ohara ls.

MARYLAND—Greenbrier ls.

MISSOURI—Aux Vases ss., Paint Creek fm., Renault fm., and Yankeetown chert

MONTANA—Monitor Mountain ls. (upper part) and Otter fm. (lower part)

NEVADA—Bailey Spring ls. (basal part), Chainman sh. (upper part), and White Pine sh. (part)

OKLAHOMA—Batesville ss., Grand River ls., and Hindsville ls.

PENNSYLVANIA—Mauch Chunk gr. (lower part)

TENNESSEE—Gasper ls. and Ohara ls.

UTAH—Great Blue ls. (lower part), Humbug fm., and Ochre Mountain ls. (middle part)

WEST VIRGINIA—Alderson ls., Bethel ss., Cypress ss., and Gasper ls.

———

ALASKA—Calico Bluff fm. (part) and Lisburne ls. (part)

ALBERTA—Rundle ls. (upper part)

NEW BRUNSWICK—Hammond River fm. and Maringouin fm.

NEWFOUNDLAND—Agathuna ls. and Woody Cove fm.

NOVA SCOTIA—McAras Brook fm. and Windsor gr. (part)

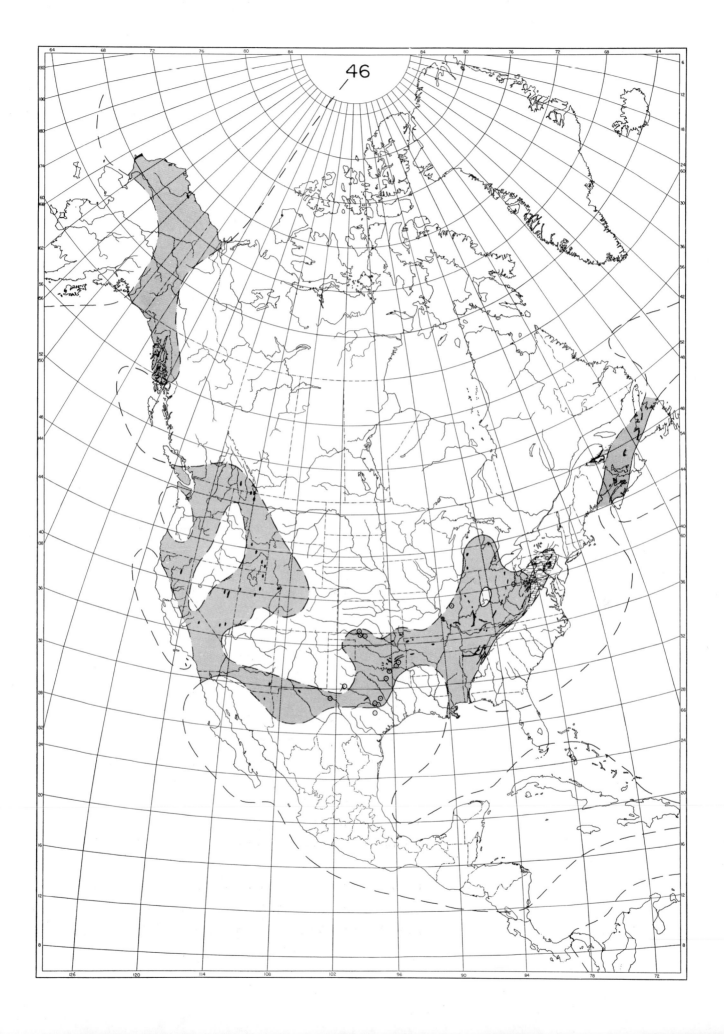

46

47

Upper Mississippian
Middle Chesterian

STRATIGRAPHIC UNITS REPRESENTED

ARKANSAS—Fayetteville sh. (part)

CALIFORNIA—Delhi fm. (lower part) and Cape Horn sl. (upper part)

IDAHO—Brazer fm. (part)

ILLINOIS—Cypress ss., Glen Dean ls., and Golconda fm.

INDIANA—Cypress ss., Glen Dean ls., and Golconda fm.

KENTUCKY—Cypress ss., Glen Dean ls., and Golconda fm.

MARYLAND—Mauch Chunk fm. (lower part)

NEVADA—Bailey Spring ls. (part), Diamond Peak qtzite. (part), White Pine sh. (part)

OKLAHOMA—Fayetteville sh. (part)

PENNSYLVANIA—Mauch Chunk fm. (lower part)

UTAH—Great Blue ls. (upper part) and Ochre Mountain ls. (upper part)

VIRGINIA—Bluefield sh. and Glen Dean ls.

WEST VIRGINIA—Bluefield gr.

WYOMING—Amsden fm. (part)

———

NEW BRUNSWICK—Maringouin fm. (upper part)

NEWFOUNDLAND—Woody Cove fm. (upper part)

NOVA SCOTIA—Windsor gr. (upper part)

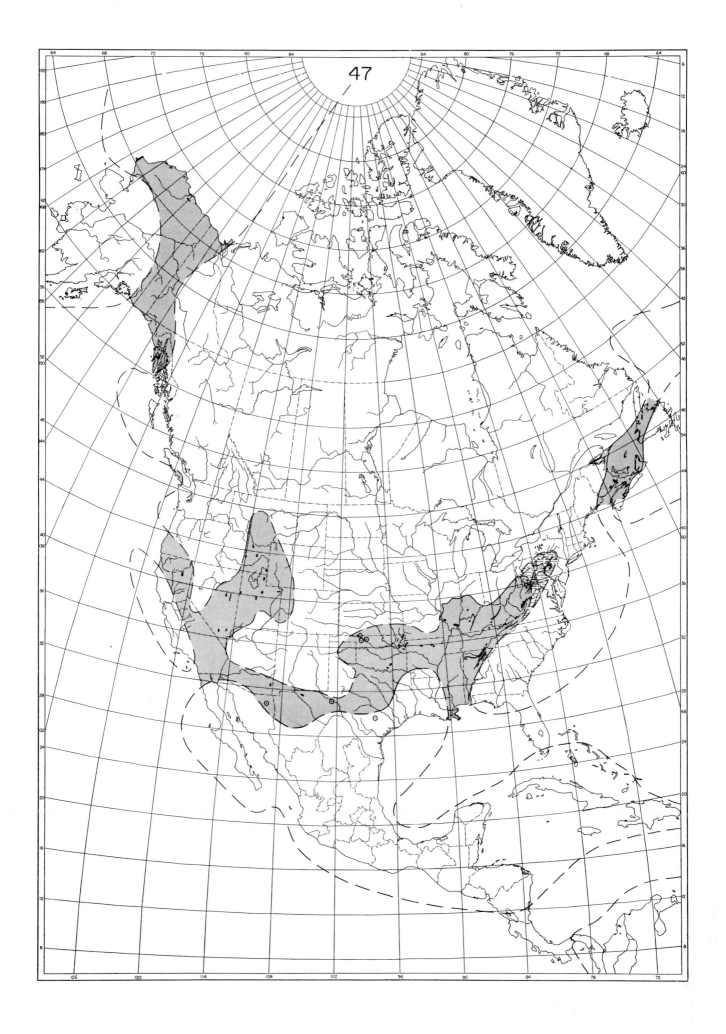

47

48

Upper Mississippian
Upper Chesterian

STRATIGRAPHIC UNITS REPRESENTED

ALABAMA—Pennington sh.

ARKANSAS—Fayetteville sh. (upper part) and Pitkin ls.

ILLINOIS—Tar Springs ss. to Kinkaid ls.

INDIANA—Tar Springs ss. to Kinkaid ls.

KENTUCKY—Leitchfield fm. and Pennington sh.

PENNSYLVANIA—Mauch Chunk fm.

TENNESSEE—Pennington sh.

VIRGINIA—Pennington fm.

WEST VIRGINIA—Hinton gr.

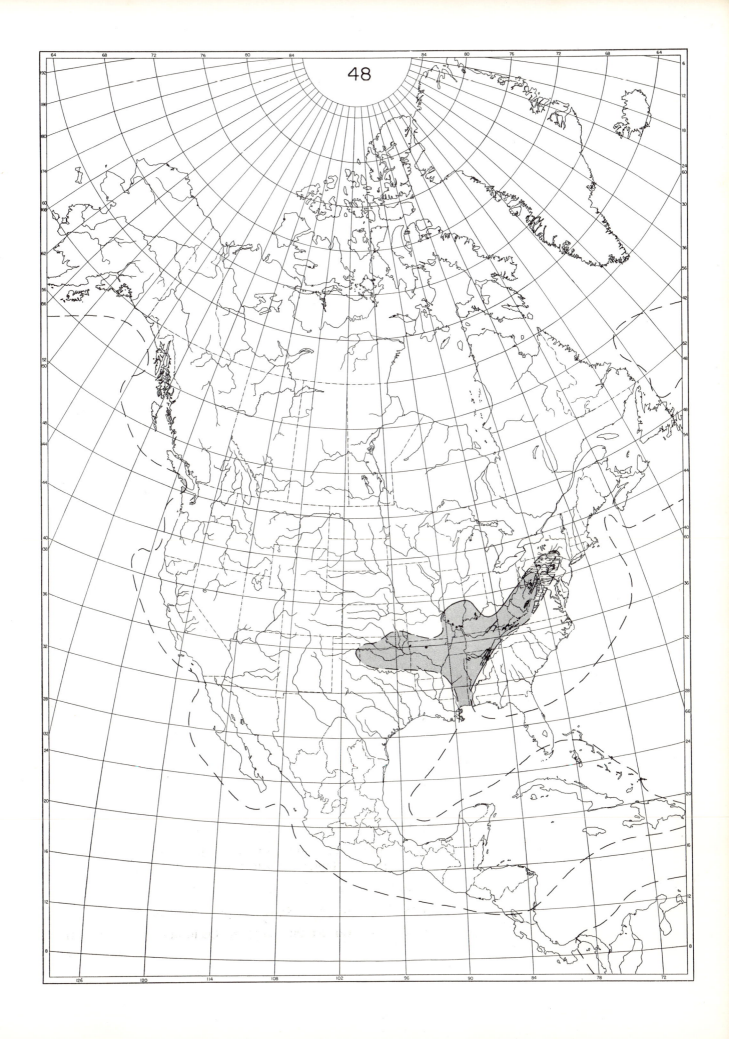

49

Lower Pennsylvanian

Lower Morrowan

STRATIGRAPHIC UNITS REPRESENTED

ALABAMA—Parkwood fm. (upper part) and Pottsville fm. (lowest part)

ARKANSAS—Jackfork ss.

IDAHO—Wells fm. (lower part)

MONTANA—Amsden fm. (part) and Quadrant fm. (lower part)

NEVADA—Bird Spring fm. (lowest part)

NEW MEXICO—Derry series (lower part) [probably post-Morrowan]

OKLAHOMA—Springer fm.

TENNESSEE—Lee fm. (lower part)

TEXAS—Marble Falls ls. (basal part) and Tesnus fm.

UTAH—Manning Canyon fm. (lower part), Morgan fm. (lower part), and Talisman qtzite. (lower part)

VIRGINIA—Lee fm. (lower part)

WEST VIRGINIA—New River gr. (lower part) and Pocahontas gr.

WYOMING—Amsden fm. (part) and Quadrant fm. (lower part)

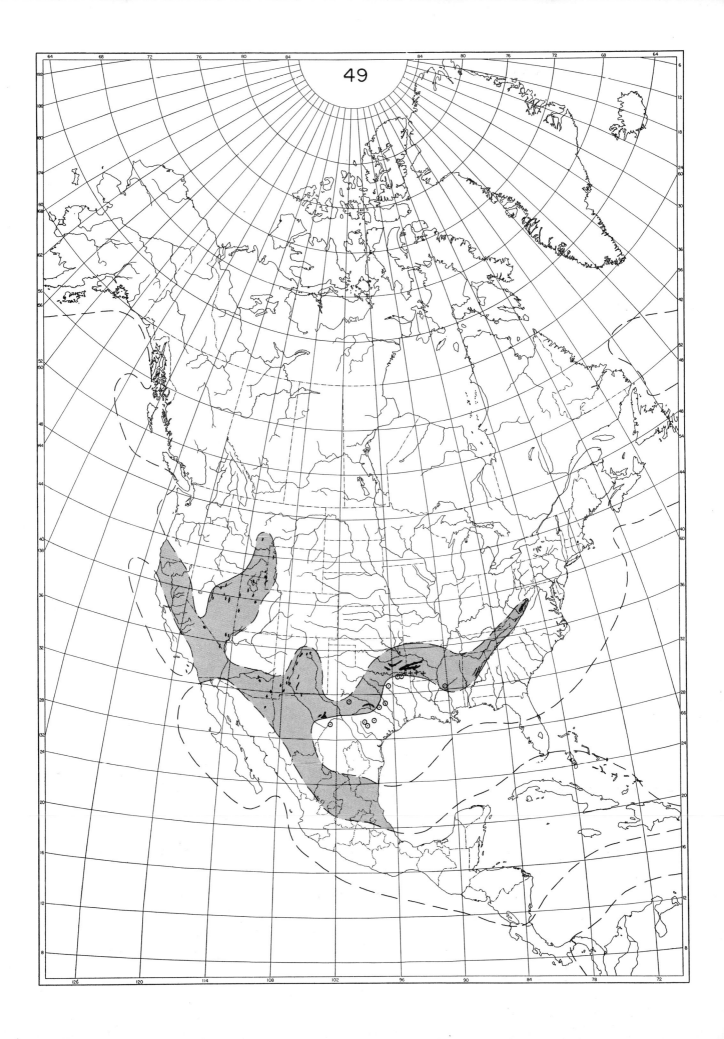

49

50

Lower Pennsylvanian

Upper Morrowan

STRATIGRAPHIC UNITS REPRESENTED

ALABAMA—Pottsville fm. (part)

ARKANSAS—Johns Valley sh. and Morrow gr.

GEORGIA—Walden fm.

IDAHO—Wells fm. (part)

ILLINOIS—Caseyville fm.

INDIANA—Caseyville fm.

KENTUCKY—Caseyville fm.

NEVADA—Bailey Spring ls. (part), Bird Spring fm. (part), Callville ls. (part), and Ely ls. (part)

OKLAHOMA—Dornick Hills gr. (lower part) and Wapanucka ls.

PENNSYLVANIA—Pottsville series (lower part)

TEXAS—Dimple ls. and Marble Falls ls.

UTAH—Manning fm. (part) and Morgan fm. (part)

VIRGINIA—Lee fm. (upper part)

WEST VIRGINIA—New River gr.

WYOMING—Amsden fm. (part) and Quadrant fm. (part)

———

NOVA SCOTIA—Harrington River deposits and Parrsboro fm.

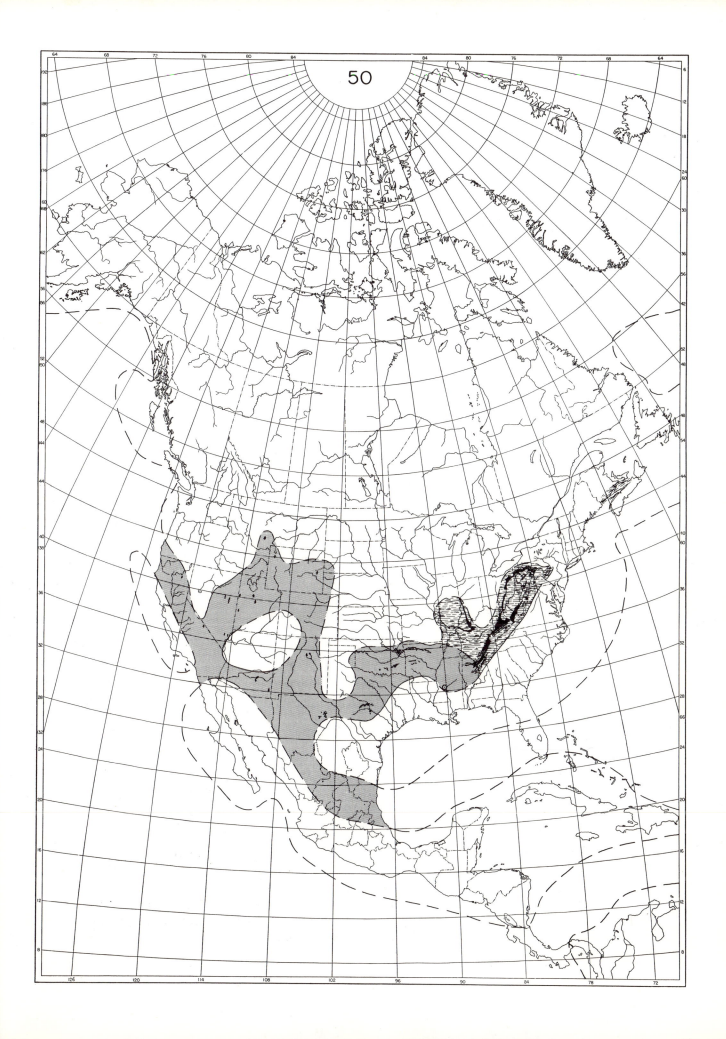

50

51

Middle Pennsylvanian

Lower Desmoinesian

STRATIGRAPHIC UNITS REPRESENTED

ARIZONA—Galiuro fm. (lower part) and Naco ls. (lower part)

COLORADO—Fountain fm. (lower part), Hermosa fm. (lower part), and McCoy fm. (lower part)

IDAHO—Weber fm. (part) and Wells fm. (part)

ILLINOIS Carbondale fm. (lower part) [Murray Bluff ss. to Stonefort ls.]

KANSAS—Cherokee sh.

MONTANA—Quadrant fm. (part)

NEVADA—Bailey Spring ls., Bird Spring ls. (part), and Callville ls. (part)

NEW MEXICO—Elephant Butte fm. and Whiskey Canyon fm.

OHIO—Allegheny fm. (lower part)

OKLAHOMA—Boggy fm., Cherokee sh. (lower part), and Savanna fm.

PENNSYLVANIA—Pottsville series (upper part)

TEXAS—Gaptank fm. (lower part) and Strawn series (lower part)

UTAH—Oquirrh fm. (part)

VIRGINIA—Kanawha gr. (upper part)

WEST VIRGINIA—Kanawha gr. (upper part)

WYOMING—Amsden fm. (part)

Editor's note: The marine-nonmarine contact from Pennsylvania to Alabama is not a line but a broad belt in which marine and nonmarine intertongue.

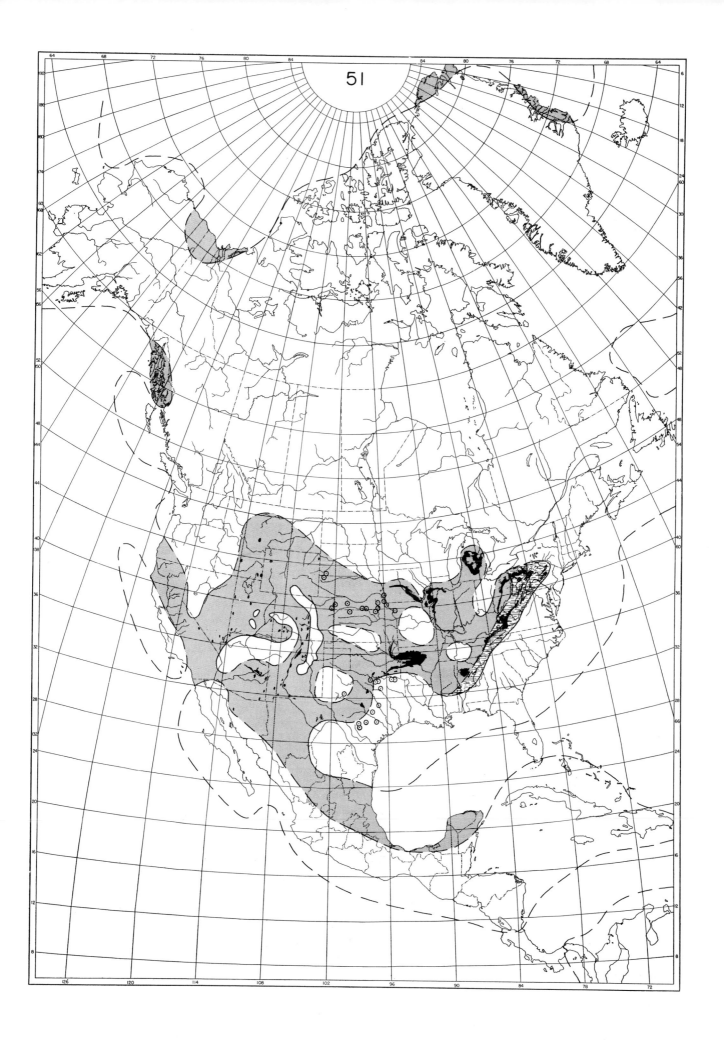

51

52

Middle Pennsylvanian
Upper Desmoinesian

STRATIGRAPHIC UNITS REPRESENTED

ARIZONA—Galiuro fm. (upper part), Hermosa fm. (part), and Naco ls. (part)

ARKANSAS—Desmoinesian series (upper part)

CALIFORNIA—Bird Spring fm. (upper part)

COLORADO—Fountain fm. (part), Hermosa fm. (part), and McCoy fm. (upper part)

IDAHO—Wells fm. (part) and Wood River fm.

ILLINOIS—Carbondale fm.

IOWA—Desmoinesian series (upper part)

KANSAS—Desmoinesian series (upper part)

KENTUCKY—Allegheny fm.

MISSOURI—Desmoinesian series (upper part)

MONTANA—Quadrant fm. (upper part)

NEW MEXICO—Bolander fm., Garcia fm., and Magdalena fm. (part)

OHIO—Allegheny series

OKLAHOMA—Desmoinesian series (upper part)

OREGON—Spotted Ridge fm. (part)

PENNSYLVANIA—Allegheny series

SOUTH DAKOTA—Minnelusa ls. (part)

TEXAS—Gaptank fm. (part) and Strawn series (upper part)

UTAH—Hermosa fm. (upper part) and Oquirrh fm. (part)

VIRGINIA—Harlan fm.

WASHINGTON—Covada gr. (part) and San Juan gr. (part)

WEST VIRGINIA—Allegheny series

WYOMING—Oquirrh fm. (part), Quadrant fm. (part), Tensleep ss. (part), and Weber fm. (part)

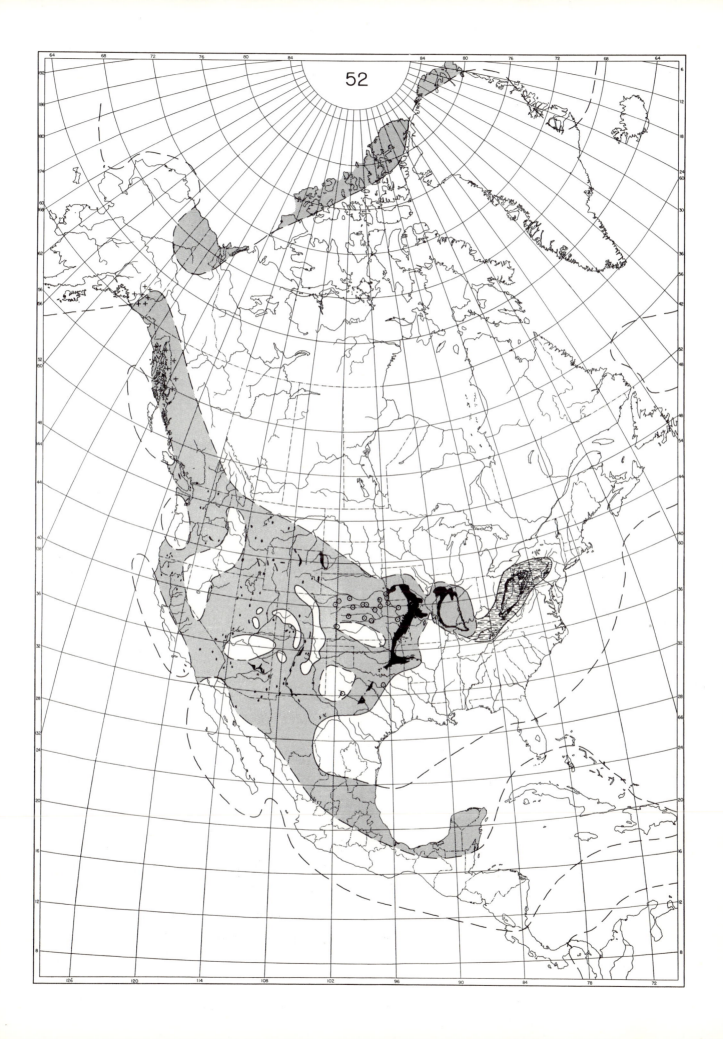

52

53

Upper Pennsylvanian
Missourian

STRATIGRAPHIC UNITS REPRESENTED

ARIZONA—Naco ls. (part)

COLORADO—Badito fm. (part), Fountain fm. (upper part), and Ingleside ls.

IDAHO—Oquirrh fm. (part), Weber fm., and Wells fm. (part)

ILLINOIS—McLeansboro gr. (part)

IOWA—Missouri series

MISSOURI—Missouri series

MONTANA—Tensleep ss.

NEVADA—Bird Spring fm. and Supai fm. (part)

NEW MEXICO—Hansonburg gr. and Verdas gr.

OHIO—Conemaugh series (part)

OKLAHOMA—Missouri series

PENNSYLVANIA—Conemaugh series (part)

TEXAS—Canyon series and Gaptank fm. (upper part)

UTAH—Oquirrh fm. (part)

WEST VIRGINIA—Conemaugh series (part)

WYOMING—Casper ss. and Tensleep ss.

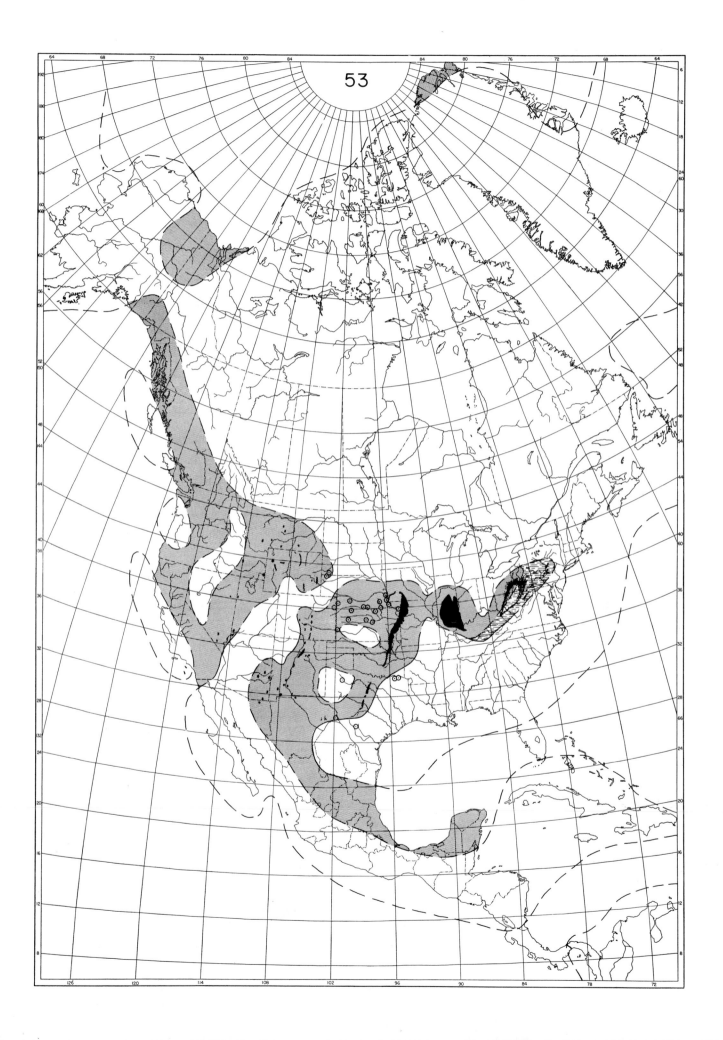

54

Upper Pennsylvanian
Virgilian

STRATIGRAPHIC UNITS REPRESENTED

IDAHO—Wells fm. (part) and Wood River fm. (upper part)

ILLINOIS—Greenup ls.

IOWA—Virgil series

KANSAS—Virgil series

MISSOURI—Virgil series

NEVADA—Bird Spring fm. (upper part)

NEW MEXICO—Fresnal gr. and Keller gr.

OHIO—Monongahela series

OKLAHOMA—Virgil series

PENNSYLVANIA—Monongahela series

TEXAS—Cisco series

UTAH—Oquirrh fm. (part)

WEST VIRGINIA—Monongahela series

WYOMING—Casper fm. (part) and Wendover gr.

Editor's note: Outcrops in western Canada are all poorly dated and may be Permian.

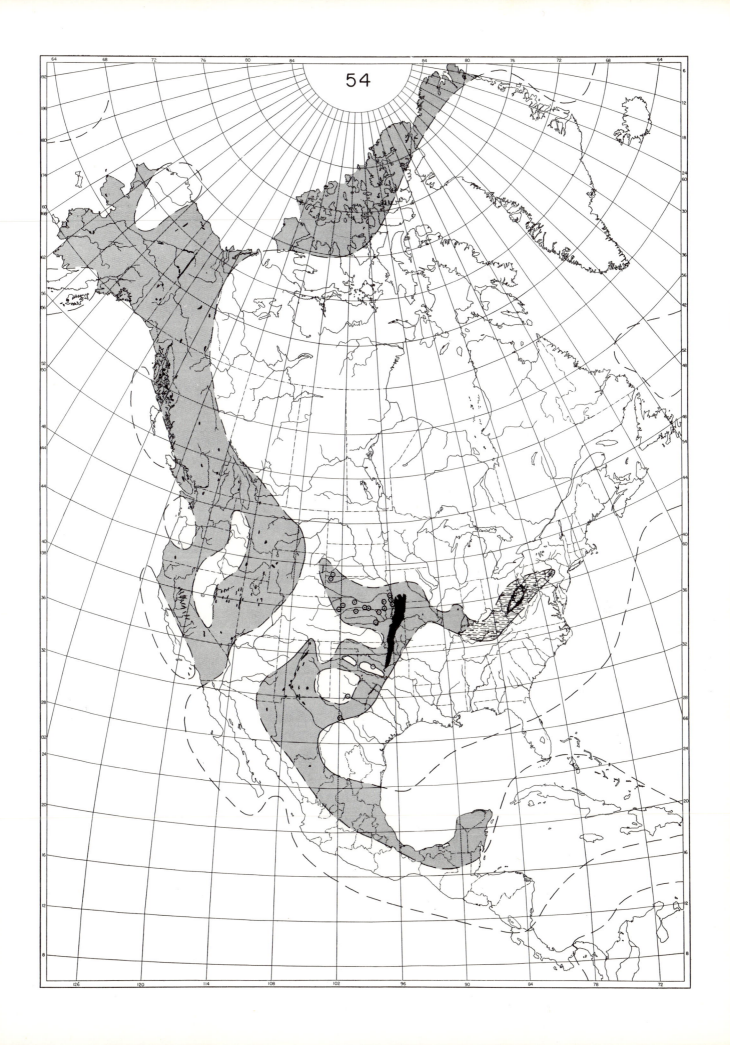

55

Lower Permian
Wolfcampian

STRATIGRAPHIC UNITS REPRESENTED

KANSAS—Admire gr., Chase gr., and Council Grove gr.

NEVADA—Bird Spring fm. (part)

OHIO—Dunkard series

OKLAHOMA—Pontotoc gr. and Wanette gr.

PENNSYLVANIA—Dunkard series

TEXAS—Admiral fm., Hueco ls., Moran fm., Pueblo fm., Putnam fm., and Wolfcamp series

WEST VIRGINIA—Dunkard series

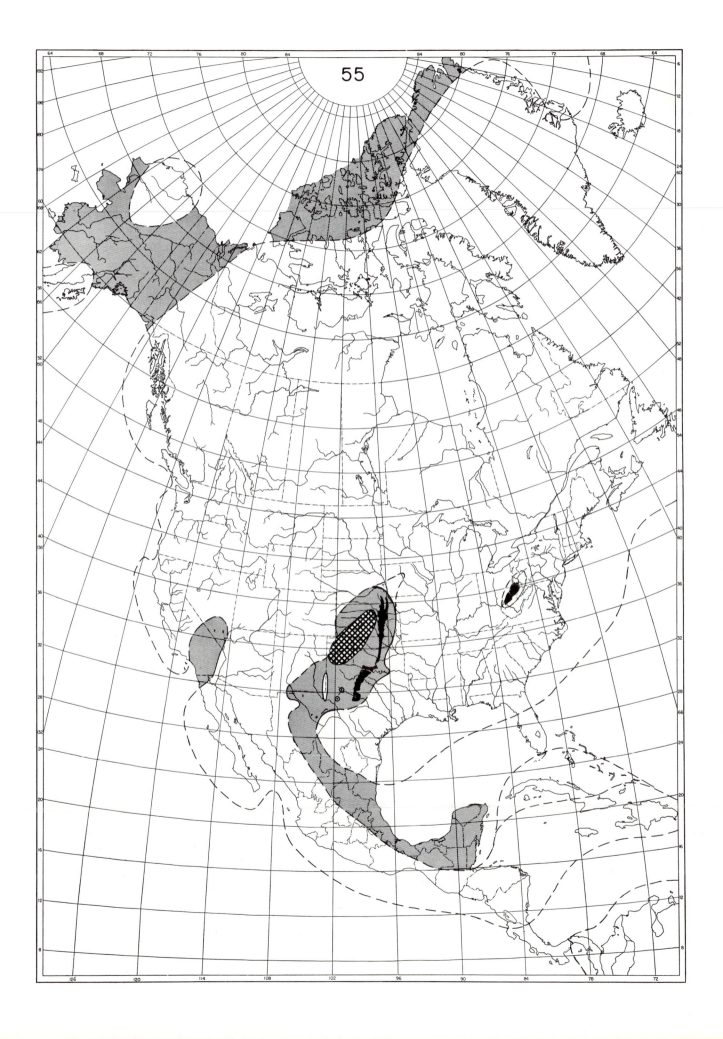

55

56

Middle Permian
Leonardian

STRATIGRAPHIC UNITS REPRESENTED

ARIZONA—Supai fm. to Kaibab ls.

KANSAS—Nippenwalls gr. and Sumner gr.

NEVADA—Supai fm. to Kaibab ls.

NEW MEXICO—Yeso fm.

OKLAHOMA—Minco gr. to Blaine fm.

TEXAS—Clear Fork gr., El Reno gr., and Leonard series

UTAH—Supai fm. to Kaibab ls., and Cutler fm.

———

BRITISH COLUMBIA—Cache Creek gr. (part)

NORTHWEST TERRITORIES—Cache Creek gr.

Editor's note: Nonmarine deposits in Wyoming represent the basal Satanka which is probably younger than Leonard and belongs to Map 57. Permian beds in California are probably of early Capitan age and should go on Map 57.

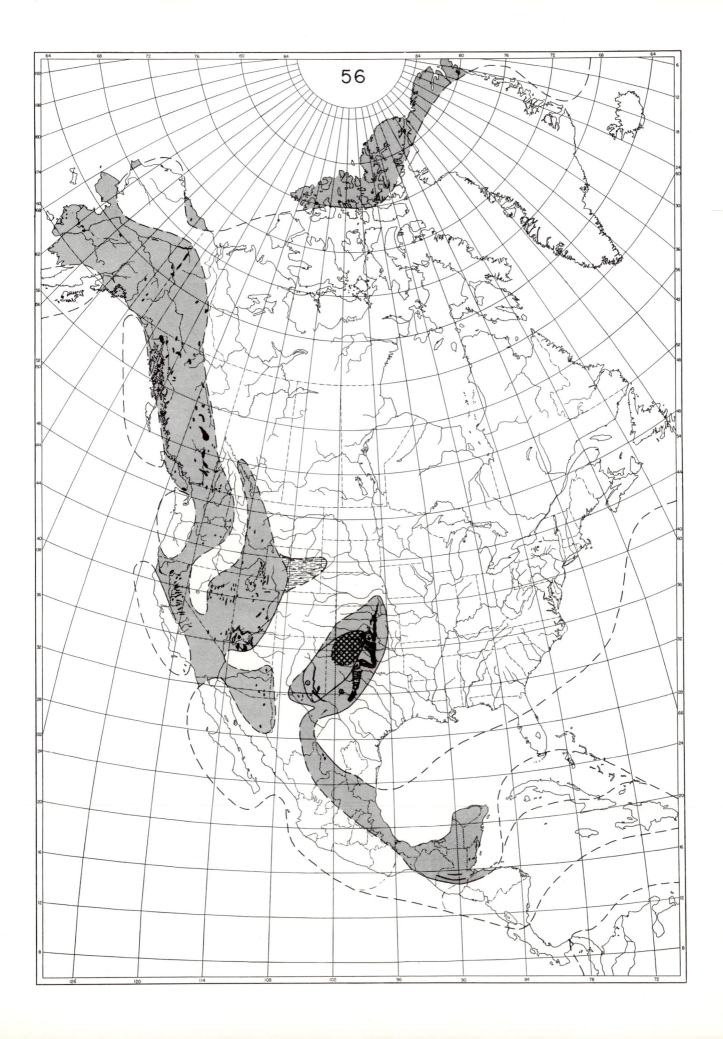

56

57

Middle Permian
Lower Guadalupian

STRATIGRAPHIC UNITS REPRESENTED

ARIZONA—Kaibab ls. (uppermost part)

CALIFORNIA—Nosoni sh.

IDAHO—Phosphoria fm.

KANSAS—Marlow fm.

NEVADA—Phosphoria fm. and Rochester trachyte

NEW MEXICO—Goat Seep ls. and San Andres ls.

OKLAHOMA—Marlow fm.

TEXAS—Brushy Canyon fm., Cherry Canyon fm., and Word ls.

UTAH—Phosphoria fm.

WYOMING—Chugwater fm. (lower part), Phosphoria fm., and
Spearfish fm.

———

ALBERTA—Cache Creek gr. (part)

BRITISH COLUMBIA—Cache Creek gr. (part)

NORTHWEST TERRITORIES—Cache Creek gr. (part)

———

GUATEMALA—["Carboniferous ls.," dated by fusulines as early
Guadalupian]

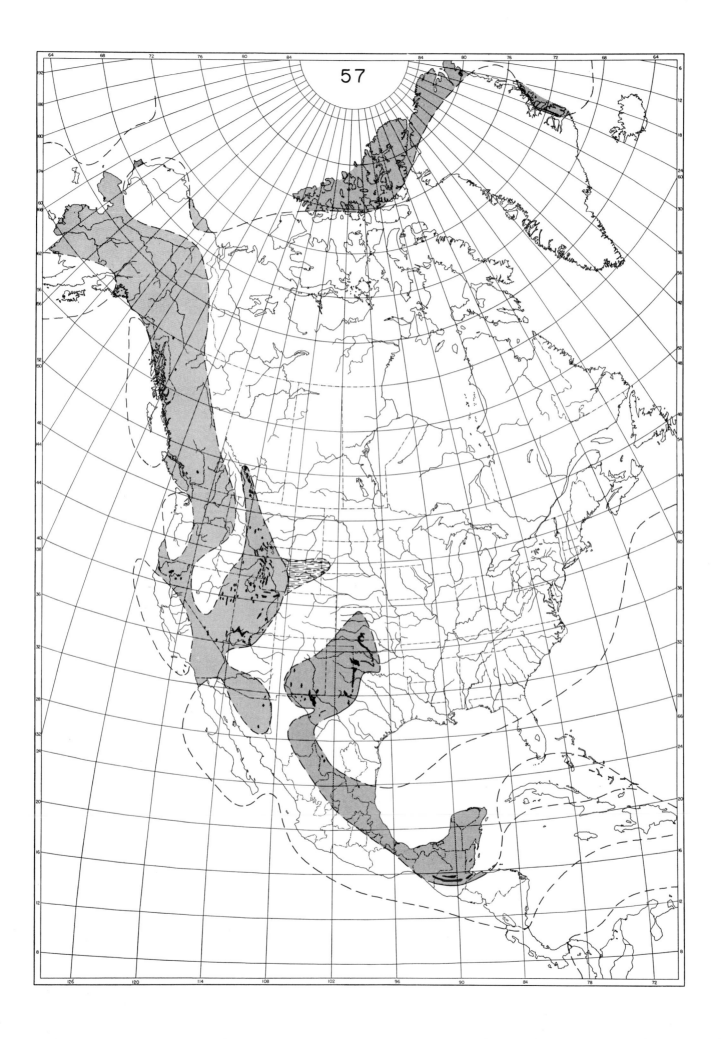

57

58

Middle Permian

Upper Guadalupian

STRATIGRAPHIC UNITS REPRESENTED

KANSAS—Whitehorse gr.

NEW MEXICO—Capitan ls. and Chalk Bluff gr.

OKLAHOMA—Whitehorse gr.

TEXAS—Bell Canyon fm., Capitan ls., and Whitehorse gr.

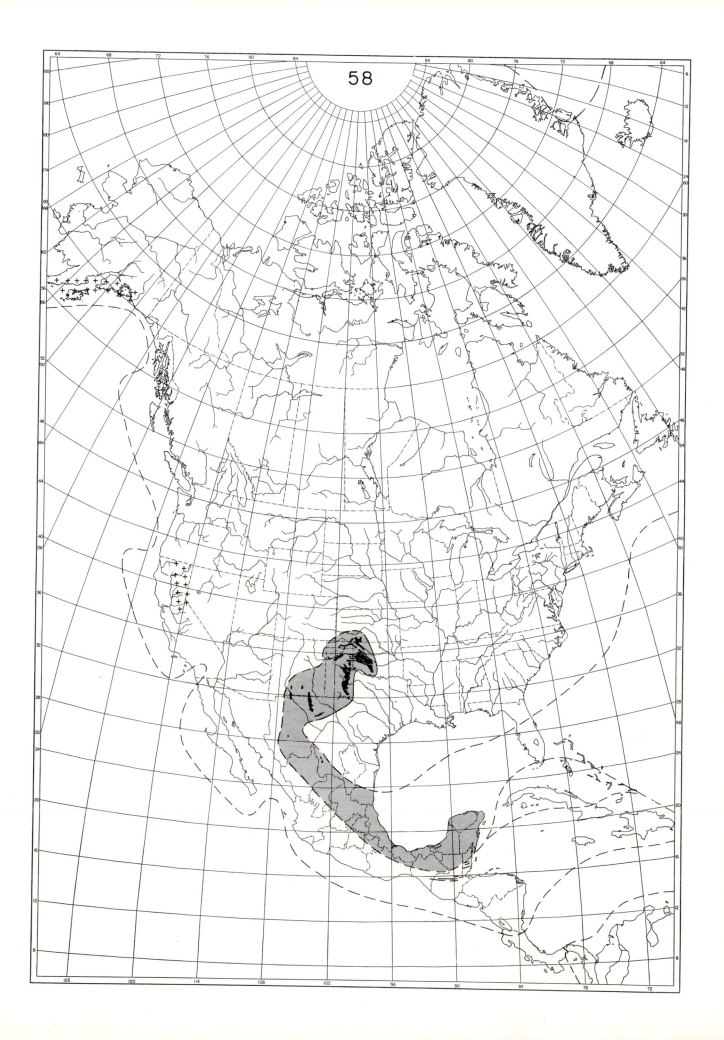

59

Lower Triassic
Otoceras Zone

STRATIGRAPHIC UNITS REPRESENTED

IDAHO—Woodside sh.

MONTANA—Woodside sh.

NEVADA—Candelaria fm. (basal part)

UTAH—Woodside sh.

WYOMING—Chugwater fm. (part) and Dinwoody fm.

GREENLAND—Eotriassic beds

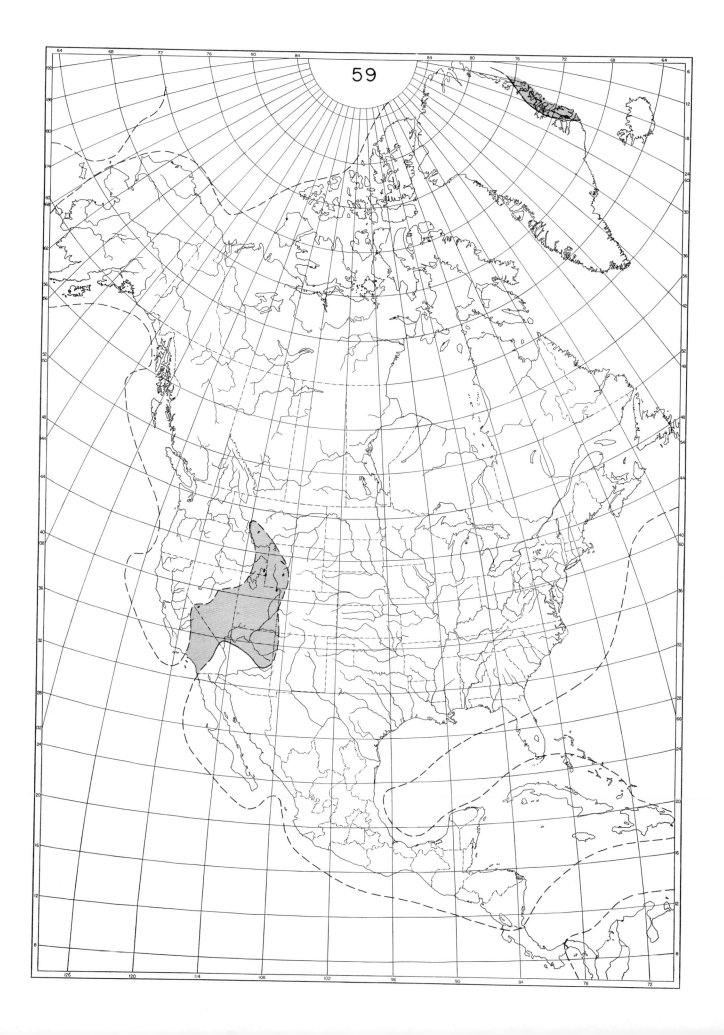

59

60
Lower Triassic
Meekoceras Zone

STRATIGRAPHIC UNITS REPRESENTED

ARIZONA—Moenkopi fm. and Virgin ls.

IDAHO—Thaynes ls.

MONTANA—Chugwater sh.

NEVADA—Moenkopi fm. (including Virgin ls.)

UTAH—Red Wash fm. and Thaynes ls.

WYOMING—Chugwater sh. and Thaynes ls.

———

ALBERTA—Spray River fm.

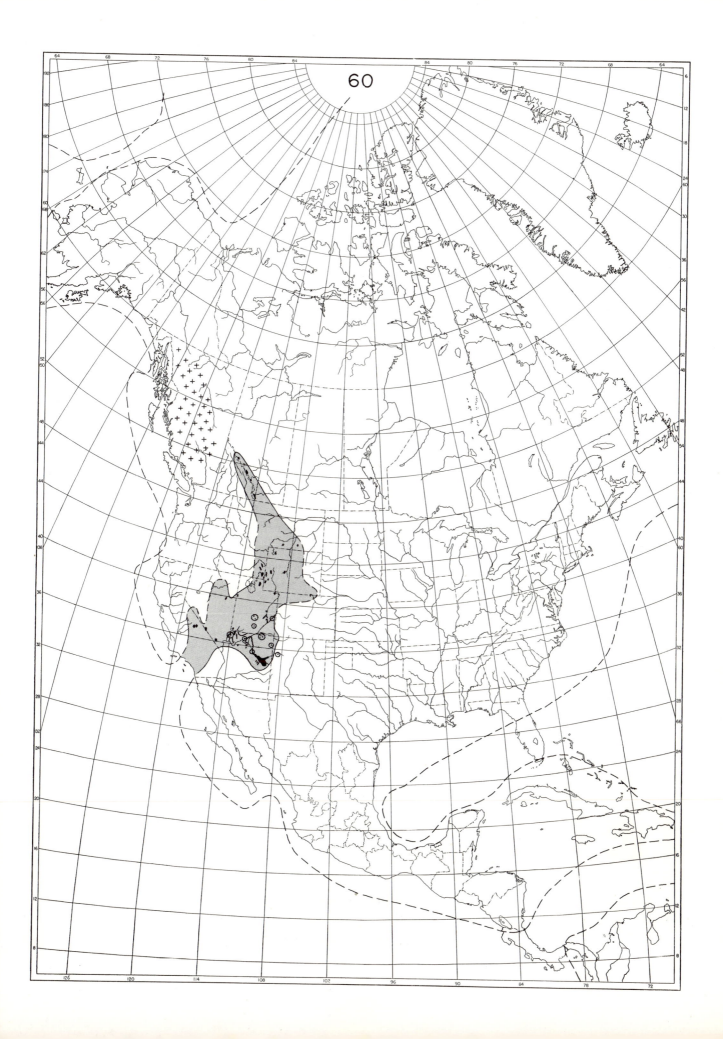

60

61

Middle Triassic

STRATIGRAPHIC UNITS REPRESENTED

CALIFORNIA—Pit sh.

IDAHO—Ankareh sh.

NEVADA—Excelsior fm.

UTAH—Red Wash fm. (upper part)

WYOMING—Chugwater sh. (upper part)

———

BRITISH COLUMBIA—Toad fm. (upper part)

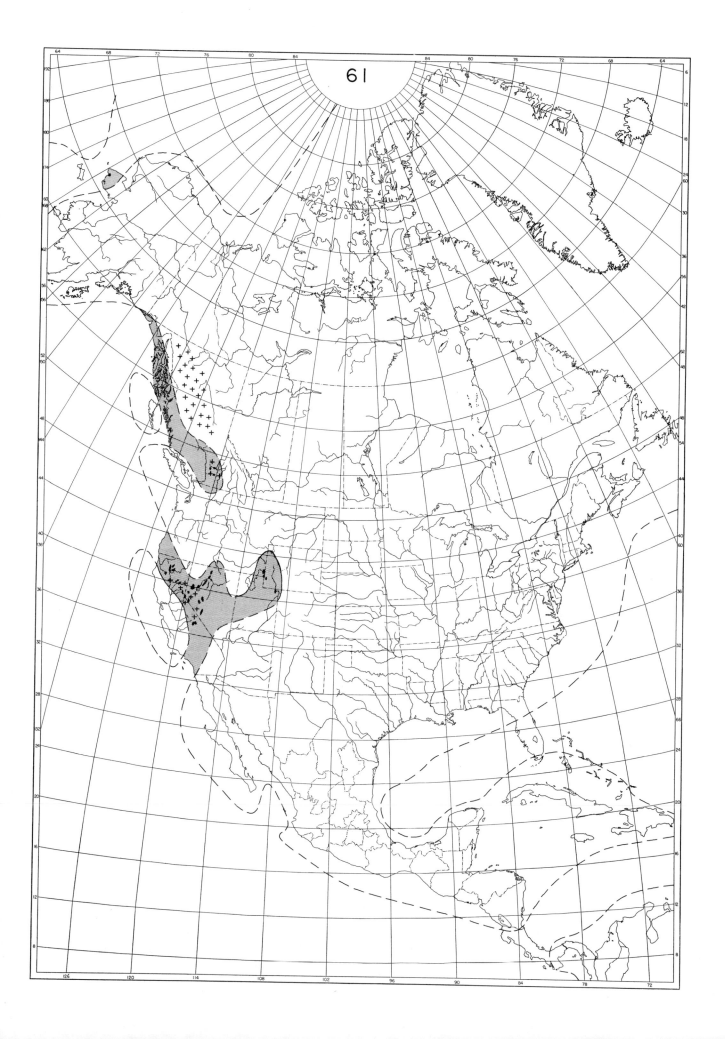

61

62

Upper Triassic
Karnian

STRATIGRAPHIC UNITS REPRESENTED

ARIZONA—Chinle sh.

CALIFORNIA—Hosselkus ls. and Pit sh. (upper part)

NEVADA—Luning fm.

NEW MEXICO—Chinle fm. and Dockum gr.

TEXAS—Dockum red beds

UTAH—Chinle sh. and Wood sh.

WYOMING—Chugwater sh. (uppermost part)

———

ALASKA—Lewes River gr. (lower part)

BRITISH COLUMBIA—Valdes fm., Karmutsen volcanics, King Salmon gr., Noel fm., Pardonet fm. (lower part), and Texado fm.

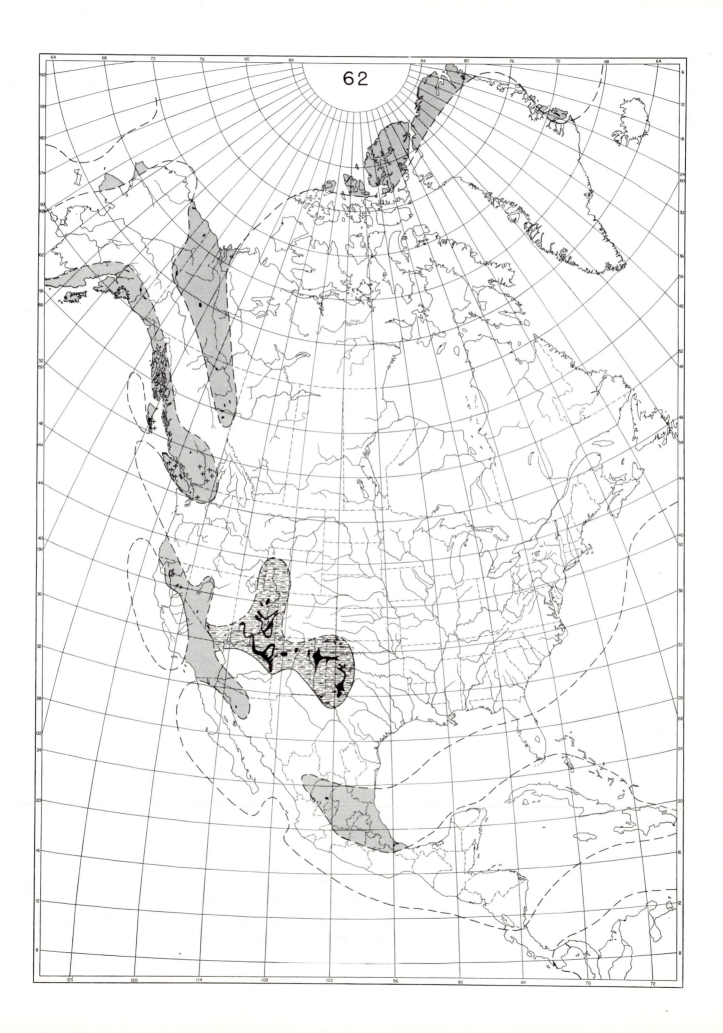

62

63

Upper Triassic
Lower Norian

STRATIGRAPHIC UNITS REPRESENTED

Appalachian region—Newark gr. (part)

Arizona—Chinle sh. (upper part)

California—Brock sh. and Hosselkus ls. (uppermost part)

Nevada—Gabbs fm. (part)

New Mexico—Chinle fm. and Dockum gr.

Utah—Chinle sh. (upper part)

———

Alaska—Chitistone ls.

British Columbia—Stuhini gr. and Takla gr.

Vancouver Island—Bonanza gr. (part), Parson's Bay fm. (part), and Vancouver volcanics (part)

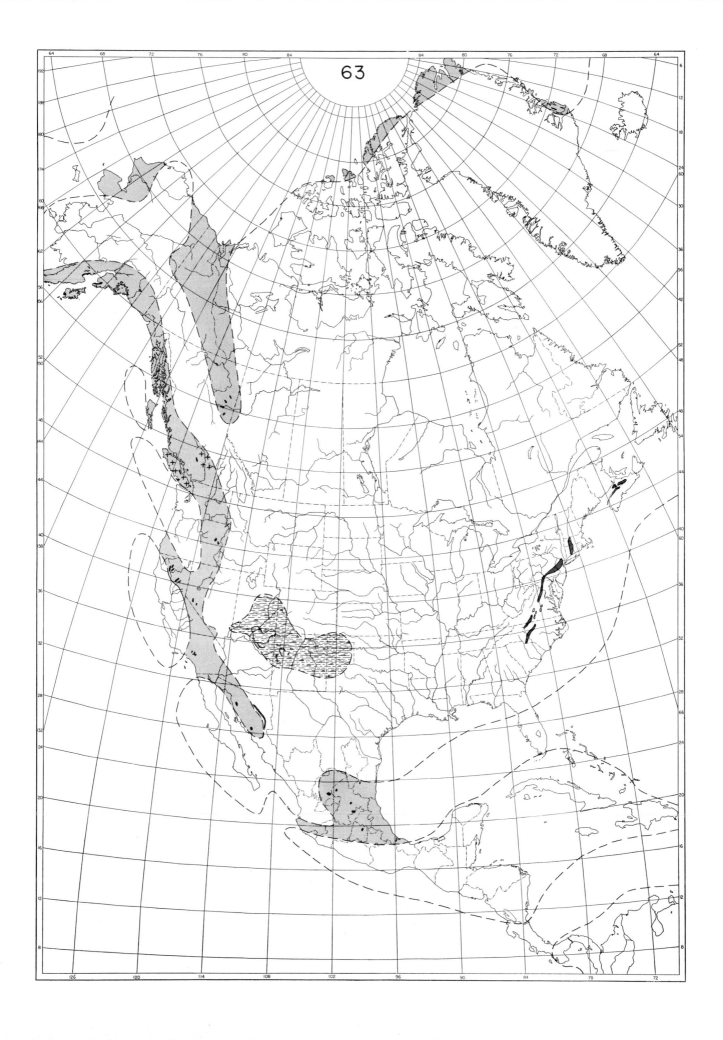

63

64

Upper Triassic

Upper Norian

STRATIGRAPHIC UNITS REPRESENTED

APPALACHIAN REGION—Newark gr. (part)

CALIFORNIA—Brock sh. and Swearinger sl.

NEVADA—Gabbs fm. (upper part)

———

ALASKA—McCarthy fm.

BRITISH COLUMBIA—Bonanza gr. (upper part), Honakta fm., Parsons Bay fm. (upper part), and Vancouver volcanics (upper part)

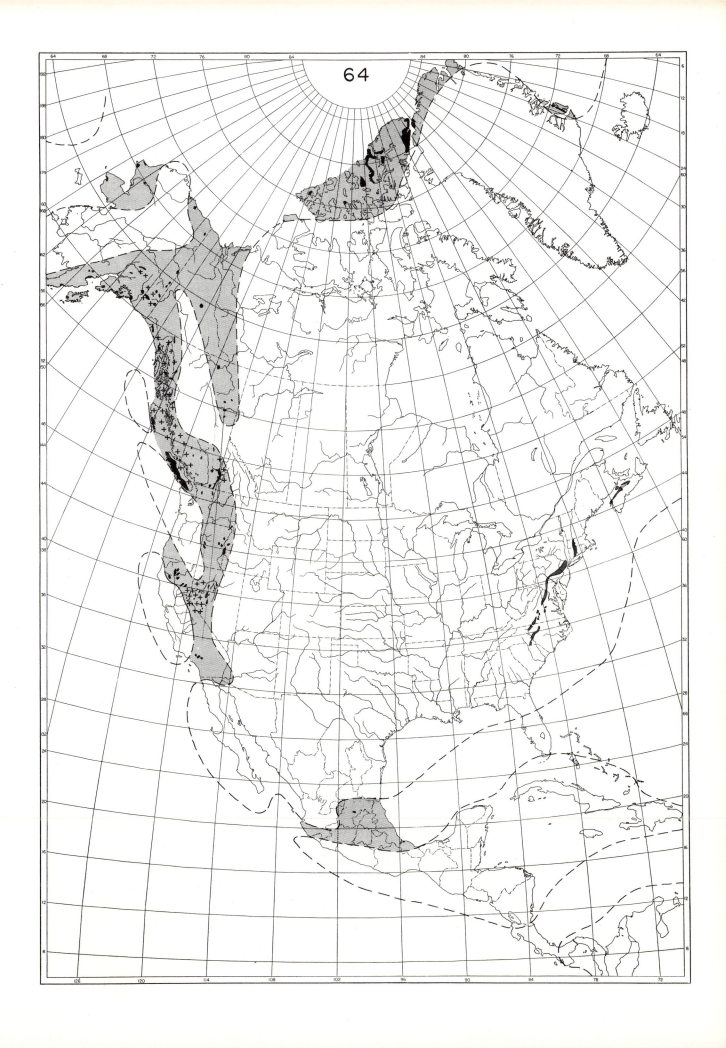

64

65

Lower Jurassic

Charmouthian

STRATIGRAPHIC UNITS REPRESENTED

CALIFORNIA—Hardgrave ss., Lilac fm., and Modin fm.

NEVADA—Sunrise fm.

OREGON—Donovan fm.

———

ALASKA—Skwentna gr. and Talkeetna fm.

BRITISH COLUMBIA—Fernie gr. (basal part)

———

MEXICO—Barranca fm. (Sonora) and Huayacocotia fm. (Vera-cruz)

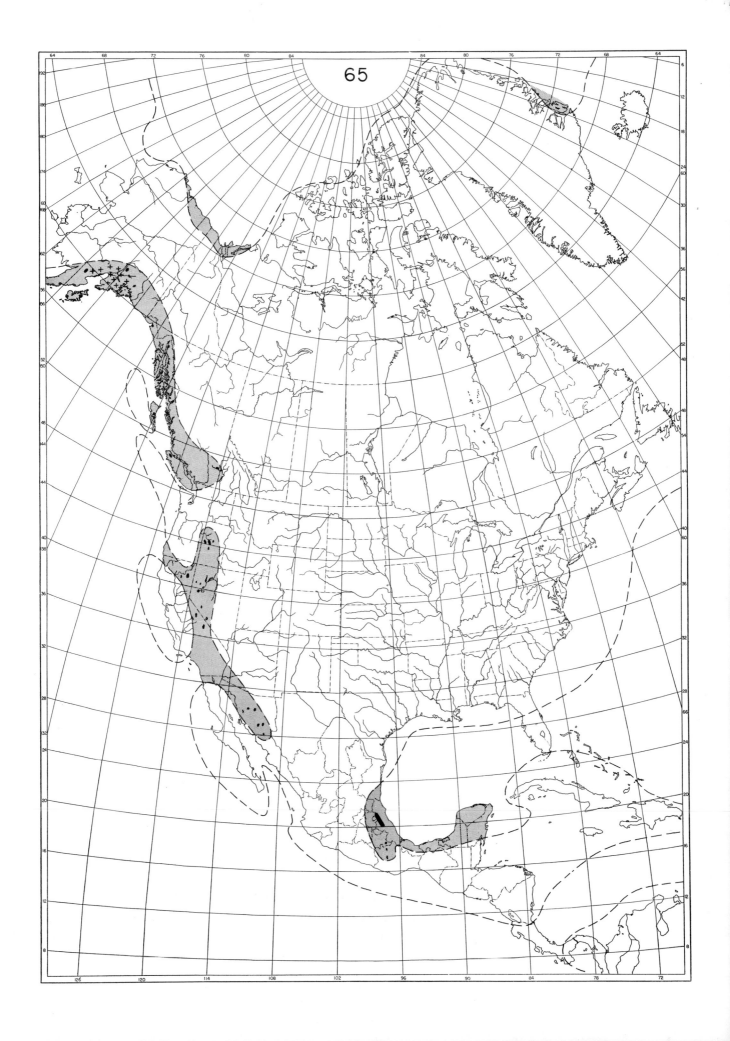

66

Lower Middle Jurassic
Bajocian

STRATIGRAPHIC UNITS REPRESENTED

CALIFORNIA—Monte de Oro fm., Mormon ss., and Thompson ls.

IDAHO—Twin Creek fm.

OREGON—Colpitts gr. and Izee gr.

UTAH—Twin Creek fm.

WYOMING—Twin Creek fm.

———

ALASKA—Tordrillo fm. (lower part) and Tuxedni fm. (lower part)

ALBERTA—Fernie gr. (Rock Creek memb.)

BRITISH COLUMBIA—Hazelton gr. (lower part), Thompson gr., and Yakoun fm. (lower part)

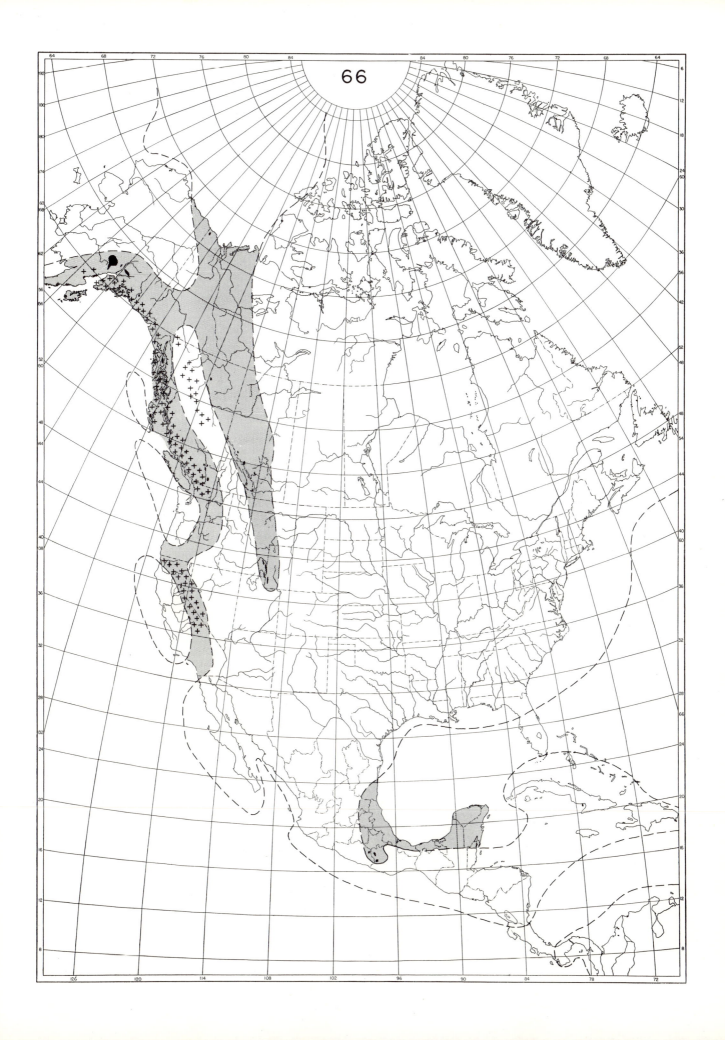

67

Upper Jurassic
Oxfordian

STRATIGRAPHIC UNITS REPRESENTED

ARKANSAS—Eagle Mills fm. and Smackover fm.

ARIZONA—Wanakah fm.

CALIFORNIA—Amador gr. (upper part), Foreman fm., and Mariposa sh.

MONTANA—Swift fm.

OREGON—Dothan gr. (upper part) and Galice group (lower part)

SOUTH DAKOTA—Redwater sh. memb. of Sundance fm.

UTAH—Curtis fm. and Summerville fm.

WYOMING—"Upper Sundance" fm.

———

ALASKA—Naknek fm. (lower part) and Treadwell sl.

ALBERTA—Fernie gr. (part)

BRITISH COLUMBIA—Hazelton gr. (part)

———

MEXICO—Huizachal fm.

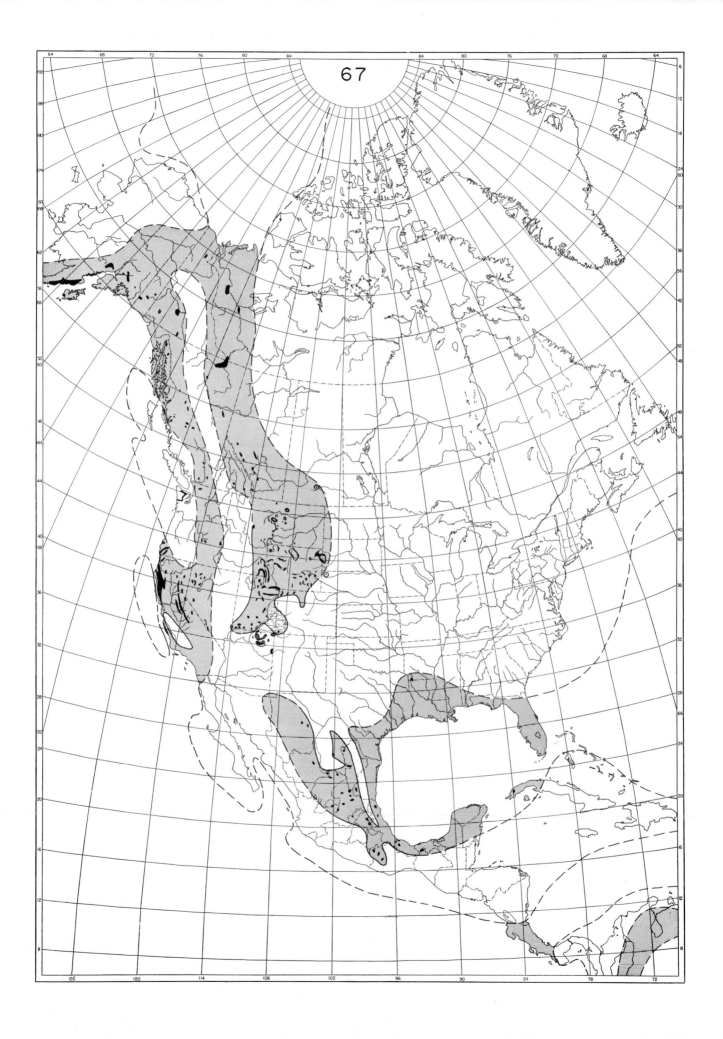

67

68

Middle Upper Jurassic
Kimmeridgian

STRATIGRAPHIC UNITS REPRESENTED

ARKANSAS—Cotton Valley gr.

ARIZONA—Morrison fm.

CALIFORNIA—Cooks Canyon fm. and Lucky S fm.

COLORADO—Morrison fm.

NEW MEXICO—Morrison fm.

TEXAS—Malone fm.

UTAH—Morrison fm.

WYOMING—Morrison fm.

———

ALASKA—Naknek fm. (upper part)

———

MEXICO—La Casita fm.

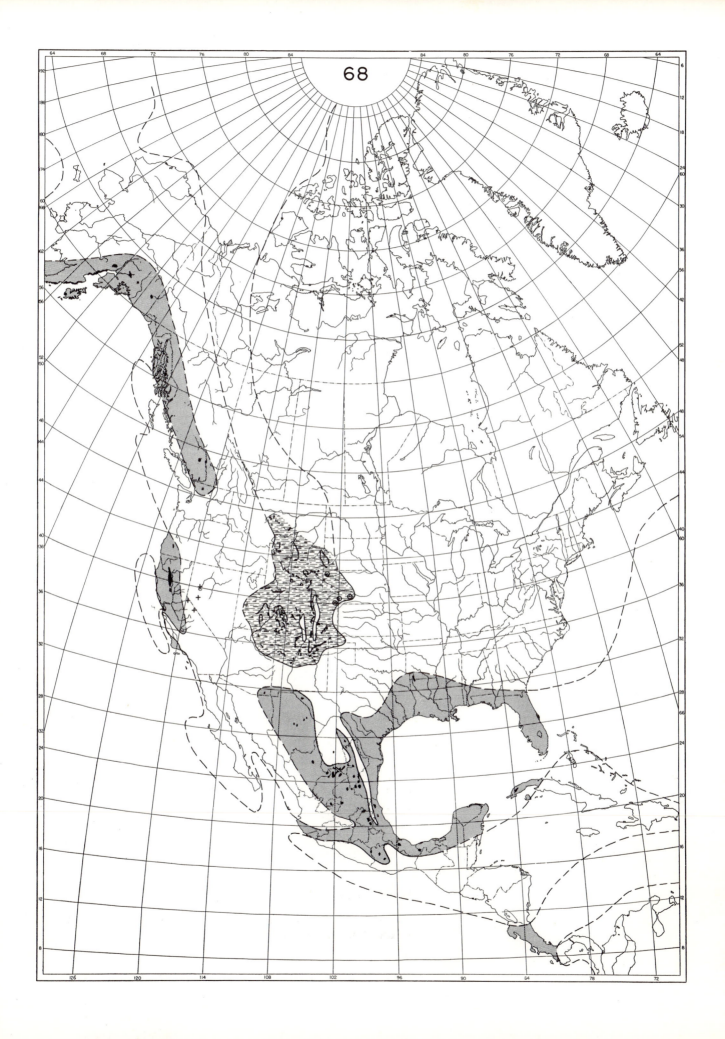

68

69

Uppermost Jurassic
Portlandian and Purbeckian

STRATIGRAPHIC UNITS REPRESENTED

CALIFORNIA—Combe fm., Granodiorite intrusives, Knoxville fm., and Trail fm.

LOUISIANA—Shuler fm.

WASHINGTON—Granodiorite intrusives

———

BRITISH COLUMBIA—Granodiorite intrusives in Coast Ranges.

———

CUBA—Vinales ls.

MEXICO—La Caja fm. (upper part), La Casita fm. (upper part), and Pimienta fm.

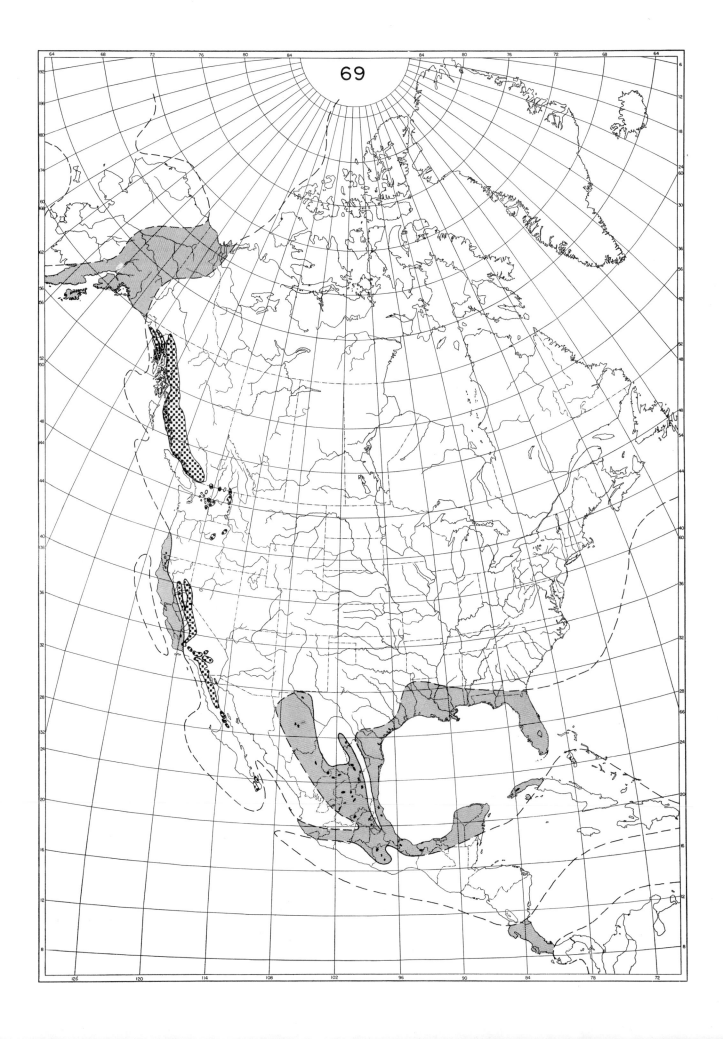

69

70

Lower Cretaceous

Lower Comanchean

STRATIGRAPHIC UNITS REPRESENTED

ARKANSAS—Trinity gr.

MARYLAND—Patapsco fm.

OKLAHOMA—Trinity sand

TEXAS—Glen Rose ls., Travis Peak fm., and Trinity gr.

———

MEXICO—Cobán ls. (lower part), La Peña fm. (upper part), San Juan Raya fm., and Tamaulipas ls.

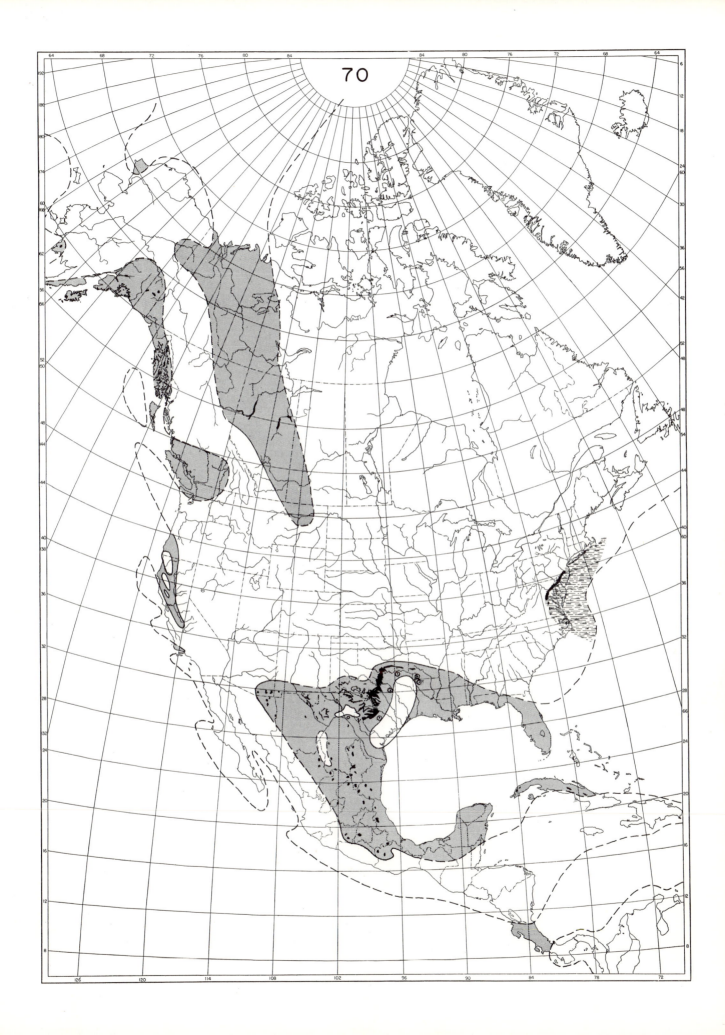

70

71

Lower Cretaceous
Middle Comanchean

STRATIGRAPHIC UNITS REPRESENTED

ARKANSAS—Goodland ls.

CALIFORNIA—Horsetown fm. (middle part)

DELAWARE—Patapsco fm.

MARYLAND—Patapsco fm.

OKLAHOMA—Goodland ls.

OREGON—Myrtle fm. (lower part)

SOUTH DAKOTA—Dakota fm.

TEXAS—Fredericksburg gr.

VIRGINIA—Patapsco fm.

———

ALBERTA—Kootenai fm.

———

CENTRAL AMERICA—Cobán ls. (part)

MEXICO—Aurora ls. (lower part)

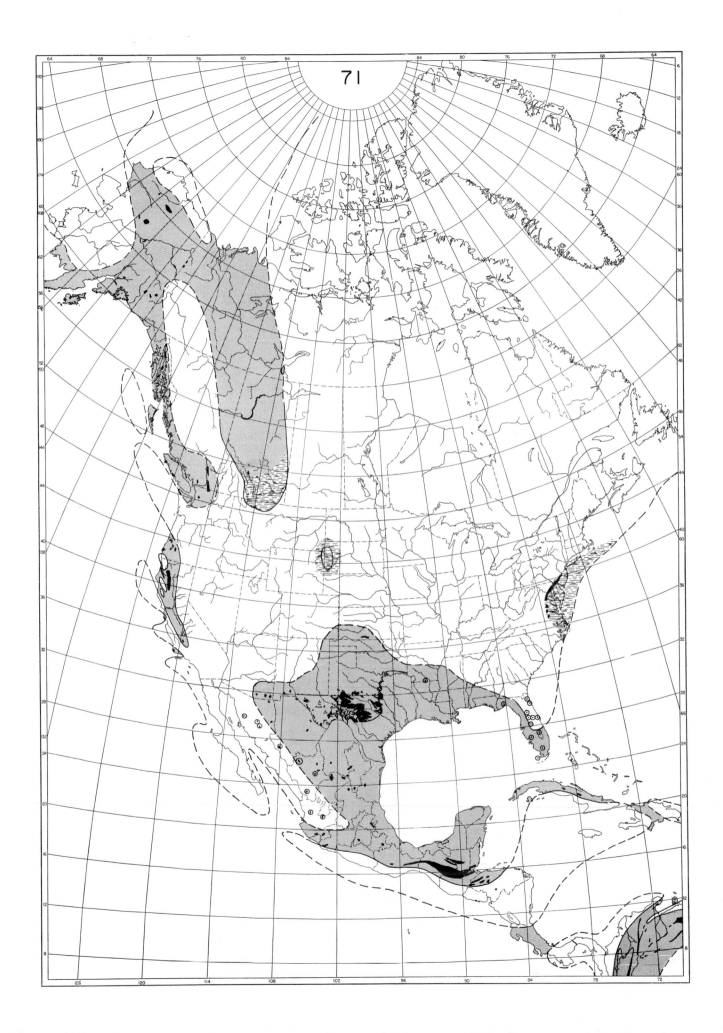

71

72

Lower Cretaceous

Upper Comanchean

STRATIGRAPHIC UNITS REPRESENTED

CALIFORNIA—Horsetown fm. (middle part) and Shasta fm. (upper part)

COLORADO—Dakota ss. (part) and Graneros sh.

KANSAS—Dakota ss. (part) and Graneros sh.

MONTANA—Mowry sh.

NEW MEXICO—Dakota ss.

OKLAHOMA—Purgatoire fm. and Washita gr.

OREGON—Myrtle fm. (upper part)

SOUTH DAKOTA—Mowry sh. and Newcastle ss.

TEXAS—Washita gr.

WYOMING—Mowry sh. and Thermopolis sh.

———

ALBERTA—Kootenai fm.

———

CENTRAL AMERICA—Cobán ls. (part)

MEXICO—Cipiapa ls., Cobán ls. (part), Sierra Madre ls. (part), and Tamulipas ls. (part)

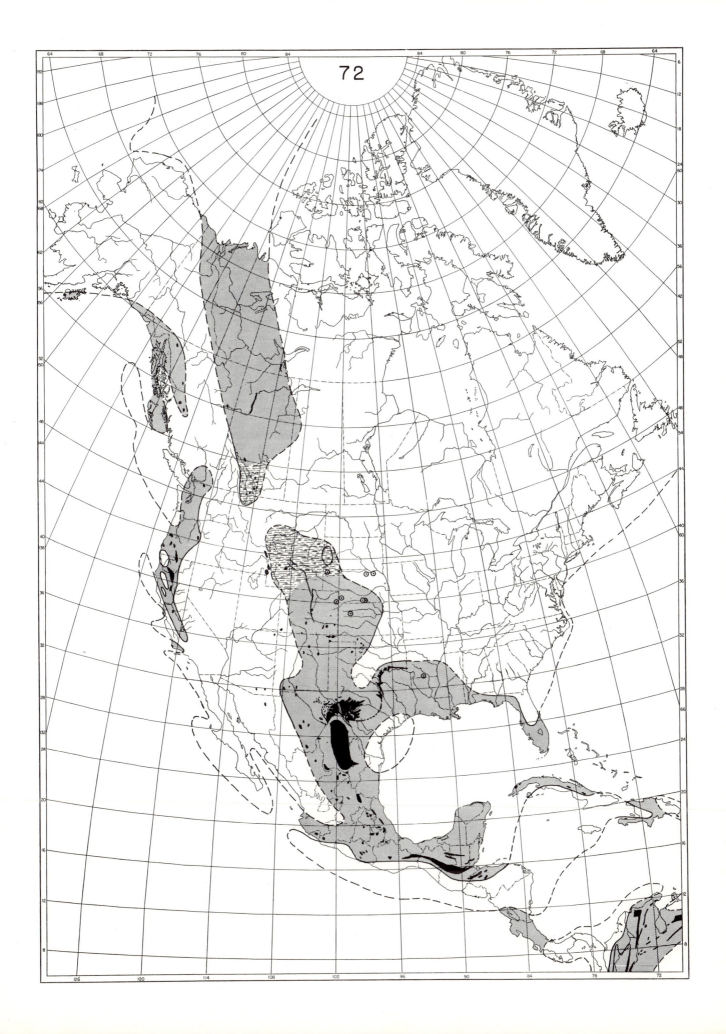

73

Lower Upper Cretaceous
Turonian

STRATIGRAPHIC UNITS REPRESENTED

ARIZONA—Mancos sh. (part) and Mesaverde fm. (lower part)

CALIFORNIA—Chico fm.

IOWA—Carlile sh. and Greenhorn ls.

KANSAS—Carlile sh. and Greenhorn ls.

MONTANA—Colorado sh. (part)

NEBRASKA—Carlile sh. and Greenhorn ls.

NEW MEXICO—Mancos sh.

NORTH DAKOTA—Benton sh. (upper part), Carlile sh., and Greenhorn ls.

OKLAHOMA—Eagle Ford sh.

SOUTH DAKOTA—Carlile sh. and Greenhorn ls.

TEXAS—Eagle Ford sh.

UTAH—Frontier ss. (part), Indianola gr. (middle part), and Mancos sh. (part)

WYOMING—Carlile sh., Frontier fm. (upper part), and Greenhorn ls.

———

MEXICO—Agua Nueva fm. (upper part), Cobán ls. (upper part), Escamela ls. (upper part), and Indidura fm. (upper part)

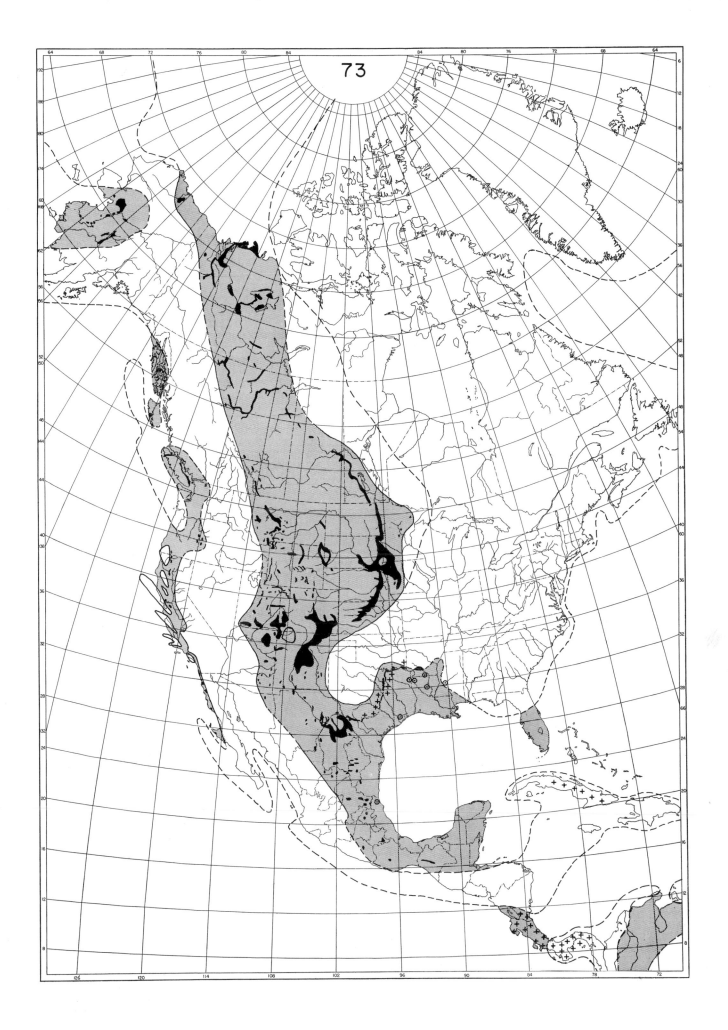

73

74

Upper Cretaceous
Lower Senonian (Niobrarian)

STRATIGRAPHIC UNITS REPRESENTED

ALABAMA—Eutaw fm.

ARIZONA—Mesaverde fm. (upper part)

ARKANSAS—Tokio fm.

COLORADO—Mancos sh. (part) and Niobrara fm.

DELAWARE—Magothy fm.

KANSAS—Niobrara fm.

MARYLAND—Magothy fm.

MINNESOTA—Niobrara fm.

MISSISSIPPI—Eutaw fm.

MONTANA—Cody sh. (part) and Colorado sh. (part)

NEBRASKA—Niobrara fm.

NEW JERSEY—Magothy fm.

NEW MEXICO—Mancos sh. (part), Mesaverde fm. (lower part), and Niobrara fm.

NORTH DAKOTA—Niobrara fm.

OKLAHOMA—Bonham marl

SOUTH DAKOTA—Niobrara fm.

TEXAS—Austin chalk

UTAH—Indianola gr. (upper part) and Mesaverde gr.

WYOMING—Cody sh. (lower part), Frontier fm. (upper part), and Niobrara fm.

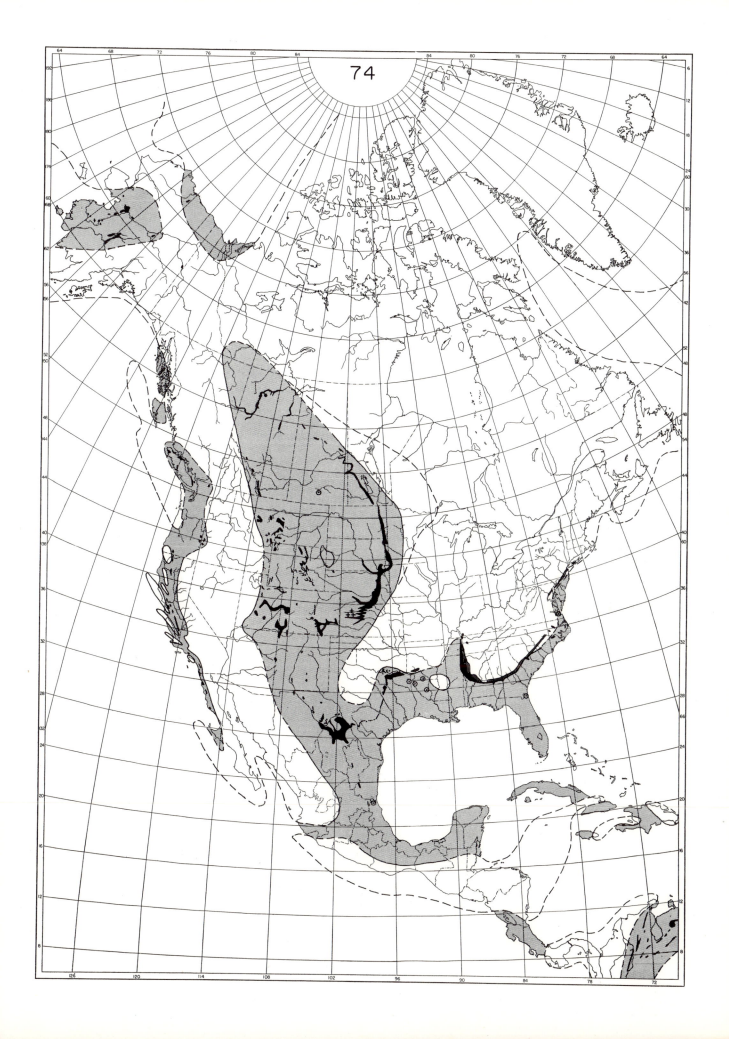

74

75

Upper Cretaceous
Campanian

STRATIGRAPHIC UNITS REPRESENTED

ALABAMA—Cusseta sand and Selma chalk

ARKANSAS—Annona chalk and Taylor marl

COLORADO—Mancos sh. (upper part), Mesaverde gr. (part), and Pierre sh.

DELAWARE—Matawan gr.

KANSAS—Pierre sh.

MARYLAND—Matawan fm.

MINNESOTA—Pierre sh.

MISSISSIPPI—Coffee sand and Selma chalk

MONTANA—Bearpaw sh., Claggett sh., Eagle ss., and Judith River fm.

NEBRASKA—Pierre sh.

NEW JERSEY—Matawan gr.

NEW MEXICO—Mesaverde fm., Lewis sh., and Pierre sh.

NORTH CAROLINA—Black Creek fm.

NORTH DAKOTA—Pierre sh.

OKLAHOMA—Annona chalk and Taylor marl

SOUTH CAROLINA—Black Creek fm.

SOUTH DAKOTA—Pierre sh.

TENNESSEE—Coffee sand

TEXAS—Anacacho ls. and Taylor marl

UTAH—Mancos sh. (upper part) and Mesaverde fm.

WYOMING—Cody sh. (upper part), Mesaverde fm., and Steele sh.

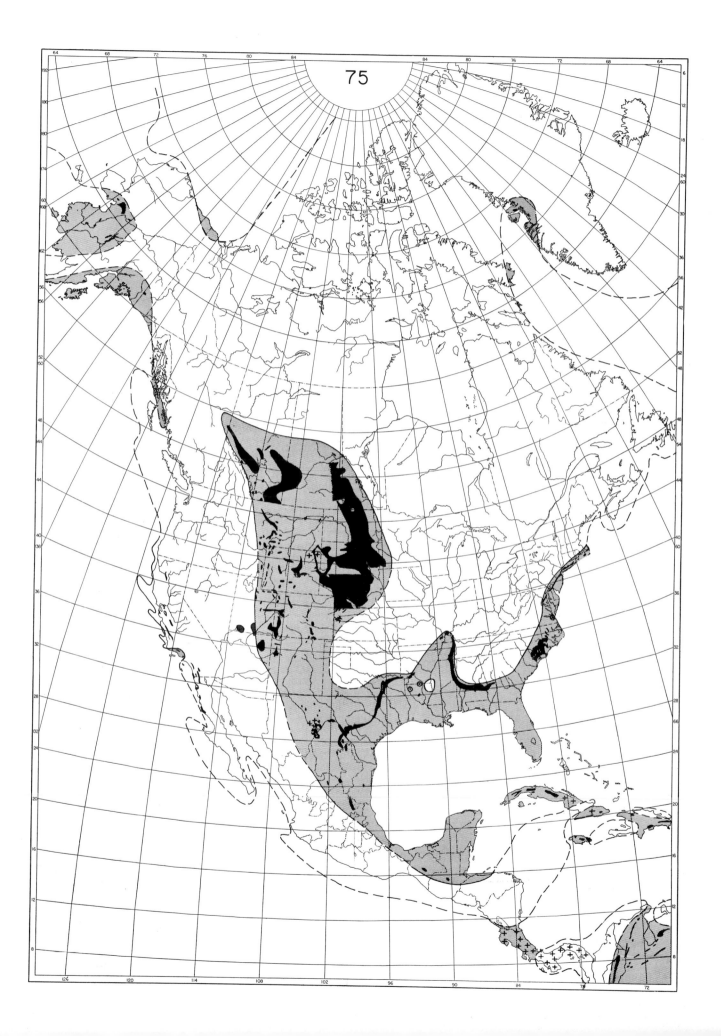

76

High Upper Cretaceous
Upper Maestrichtian and (?) Danian

STRATIGRAPHIC UNITS REPRESENTED

COLORADO—Animas fm., Fox Hills ss., Kirtland sh., Lance fm., Laramie fm., and Vermejo fm.

MONTANA—Hell Creek fm., Livingston fm. (upper part), and St. Mary River fm.

NEBRASKA—Fox Hills ss. and Hell Creek fm.

NEW MEXICO—Animas fm., Galisteo ss., Kirtland sh., Ojo Alamo ss., Raton fm., and Vermejo fm.

NORTH DAKOTA—Fox Hills ss. and Hell Creek fm.

SOUTH DAKOTA—Fox Hills ss. and Hell Creek fm.

TEXAS—Escondido fm.

UTAH—Currant Creek fm., Kaiparowits fm., and North Horn fm.

WYOMING—Lance fm. and Medicine Bow fm.

————

ALBERTA—Edmonton fm. (upper part) and St. Mary River fm. (upper part)

MANITOBA—Boissevain fm.

————

CUBA—Habana fm. (upper part)

JAMAICA—Blue Mountain series (upper part)

MEXICO—Cardenas fm. (upper part), Difunta fm. (upper part), Méndez sh. (upper part)

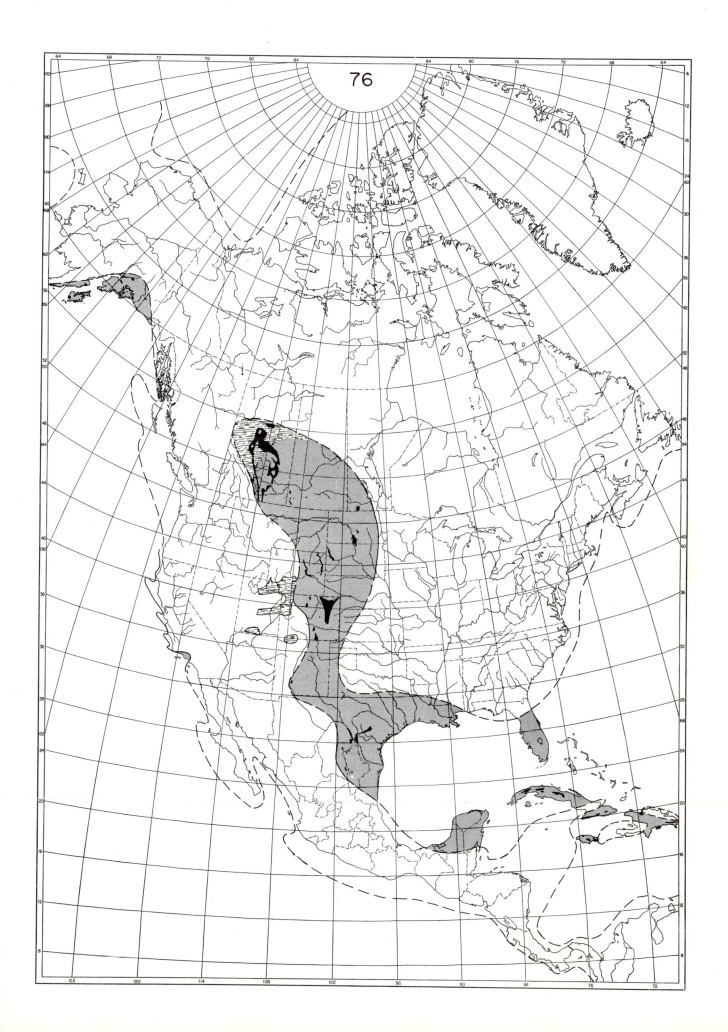

77

Lower Cenozoic

Paleocene

STRATIGRAPHIC UNITS REPRESENTED

ALABAMA—Clayton fm. and Porter's Creek clay

ARKANSAS—Midway gr.

CALIFORNIA—Lodo fm. and Martinez fm.

GEORGIA—Clayton fm.

MISSOURI—Clayton fm. and Porter's Creek clay

MISSISSIPPI—Clayton fm. and Porter's Creek clay

MONTANA—Fort Union gr. and Wasatch gr. (lower part)

NEW MEXICO—Puerco fm., Tiffany fm., and Torrejon fm.

NORTH DAKOTA—Fort Union gr.

SOUTH DAKOTA—Fort Union gr.

TENNESSEE—Clayton fm. and Porter's Creek clay

TEXAS—Midway gr.

UTAH—Flagstaff ls.

WYOMING—Fort Union gr. and Wasatch gr. (lower part)

———

ALBERTA—Paskapoo fm.

SASKATCHEWAN—Ravenscrag fm.

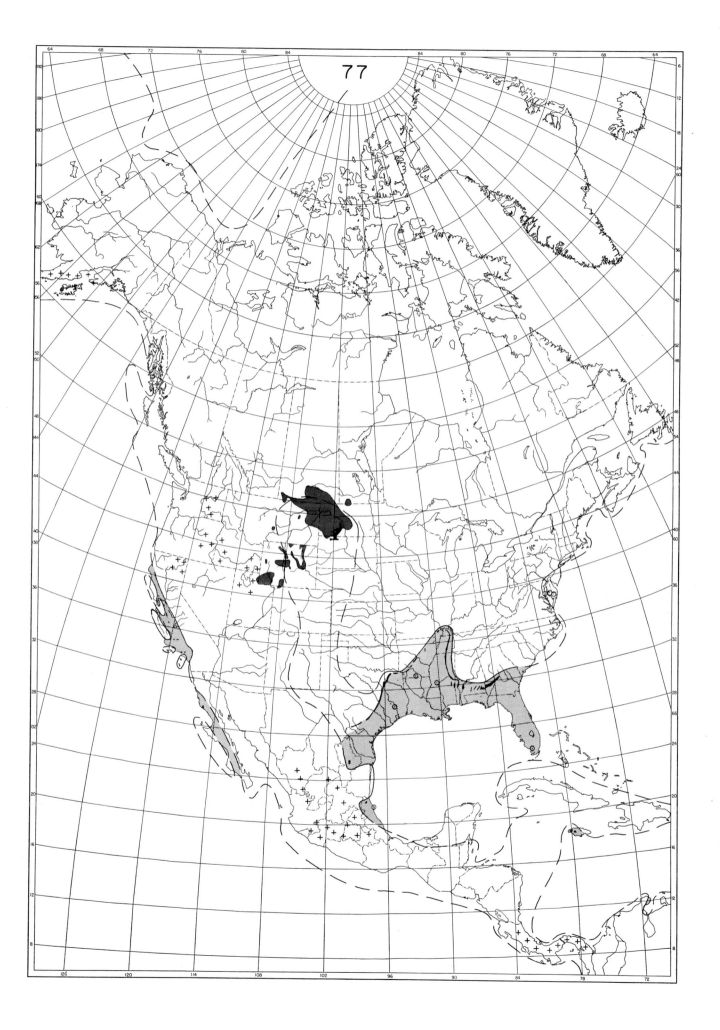

78

Lower Cenozoic
Lower Eocene (Wilcox)

STRATIGRAPHIC UNITS REPRESENTED

ARKANSAS—Wilcox fm.

CALIFORNIA—Domengine fm. and Lodo fm. (upper part)

GEORGIA—Wilcox fm.

MARYLAND—Aquia fm.

MISSISSIPPI—Ackerman fm., Hatchetigbee fm., Holly Springs ss., Nanafalia fm., and Salt Mountain ls.

NEW JERSEY—Hornerstown marl, Manasquan marl, and Vincentown sand

OREGON—Tyee fm. and Umpqua fm.

SOUTH CAROLINA—Black Mingo fm.

TEXAS—Indio fm. and Wilcox gr.

UTAH—Wasatch fm.

WASHINGTON—Cresent fm. (lower part) and Puget gr. (middle part)

WYOMING—Gray Bull fm., Green River fm. (basal part), Indian Meadows fm., Lost Cabin fm., Lysite fm., Sand Coulee fm., Wasatch fm., and Wind River fm.

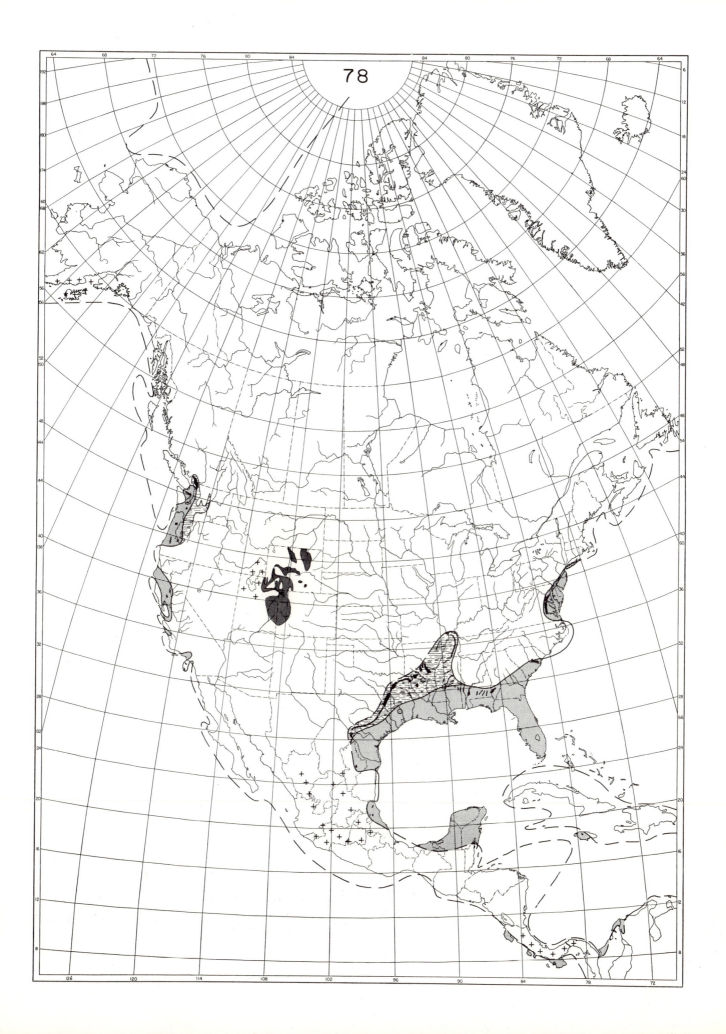

79

Lower Cenozoic
Middle Eocene (Claiborne)

STRATIGRAPHIC UNITS REPRESENTED

ALABAMA—Lisbon fm. and Tallahatta fm.

ARKANSAS—Claiborne gr.

CALIFORNIA—Kreyenhagen sh. and Tapo Ranch fm.

COLORADO—Green River fm.

GEORGIA—McBean fm.

LOUISIANA—Cane River fm., Cook Mountain fm., Sparta sand, and Yegua fm.

MARYLAND—Woodstock marl

MISSISSIPPI—Lisbon fm. and Tallahatta fm.

NEW JERSEY—Shark River marl

OREGON—Arago fm.

SOUTH CAROLINA—McBean fm.

TEXAS—Cook Mountain fm., Mount Selman fm., and Yegua fm.

UTAH—Green River fm.

WASHINGTON—Cowlitz fm.

WYOMING—Bridger fm., Green River fm., Tepee Trail fm., and Uinta fm.

Editor's note: Green River lake beds are shown in light stippling.

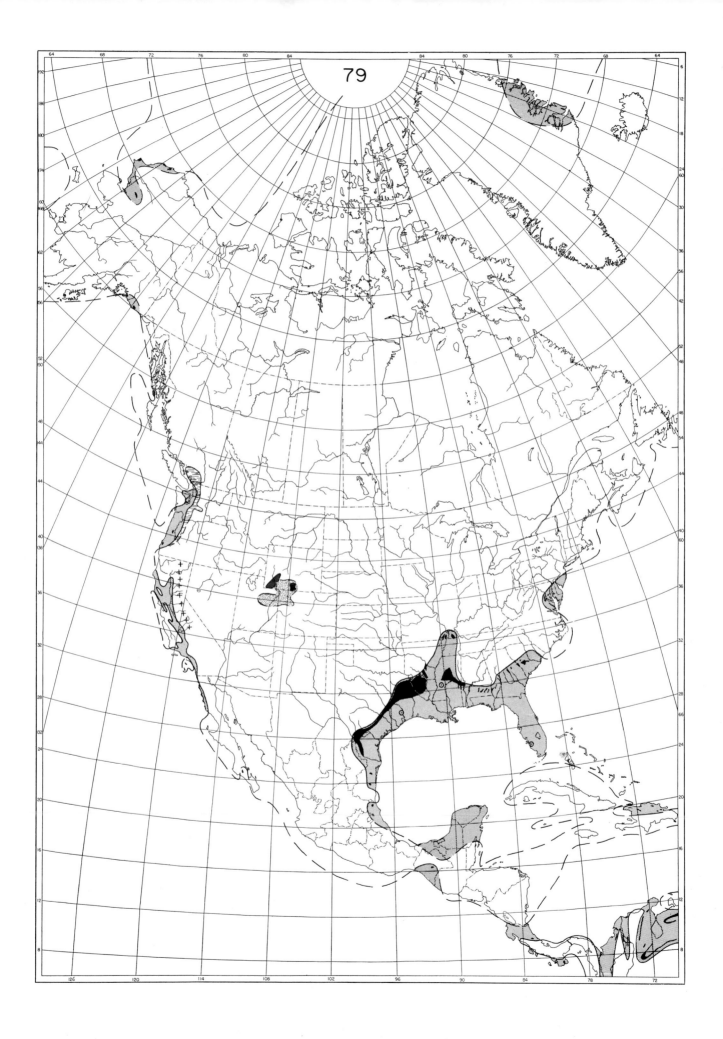

80

Lower Cenozoic
Upper Eocene (Jackson)

STRATIGRAPHIC UNITS REPRESENTED

ALABAMA—Moodys marl and Yazoo clay

ARKANSAS—Jackson fm.

CALIFORNIA—Kreyenhagen sh. (part), Markley ss. (part), and Sespe fm. (part)

FLORIDA—Ocala ls.

GEORGIA—Ocala ls.

LOUISIANA—Jackson fm.

MISSISSIPPI—Moodys marl and Yazoo clay

NORTH CAROLINA—Castle Hayne marl

SOUTH CAROLINA—Barnwell fm., Cooper marl, and Santee ls.

TEXAS—Jackson fm.

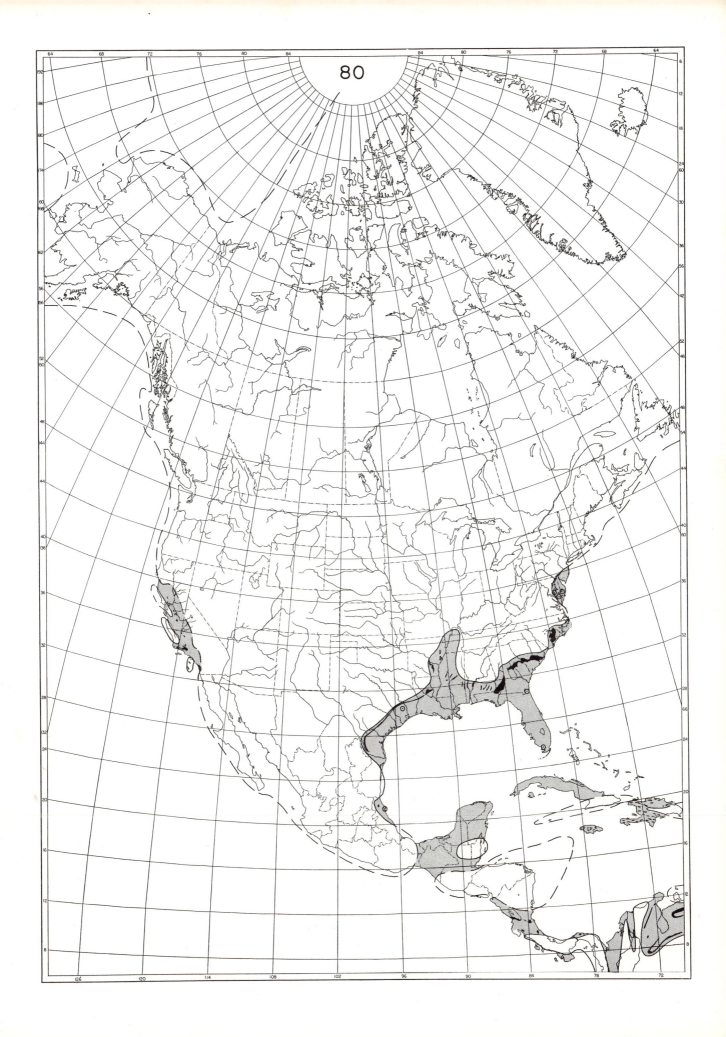

81

Middle Cenozoic
Oligocene

STRATIGRAPHIC UNITS REPRESENTED

ALABAMA—Flint River fm. and Vicksburg gr.

CALIFORNIA—Kreyenhagen sh. (part), San Lorenzo sh., Sespe fm. (part), and Titus Canyon fm.

FLORIDA—Byram ls., Marianna ls., and Sewanee ls.

GEORGIA—Flint River fm. and Sewanee ls.

LOUISIANA—Vicksburg ls.

MISSISSIPPI—Chickasawhay marl and Vicksburg gr.

MONTANA—Cook Ranch fm. and McCarty's Mountain fm. (Oreodon beds)

NEBRASKA—White River fm.

OREGON—Eugene fm., Tunnel Point ss., and Yaquina fm.

SOUTH DAKOTA—White River fm.

TEXAS—Frio clay

WASHINGTON—Lincoln fm.

WYOMING—Bates Hole fm., White River fm., and Wiggins fm.

———

DOMINICAN REPUBLIC—Tabera fm.

JAMAICA—White ls.

PANAMA—Culebra fm.

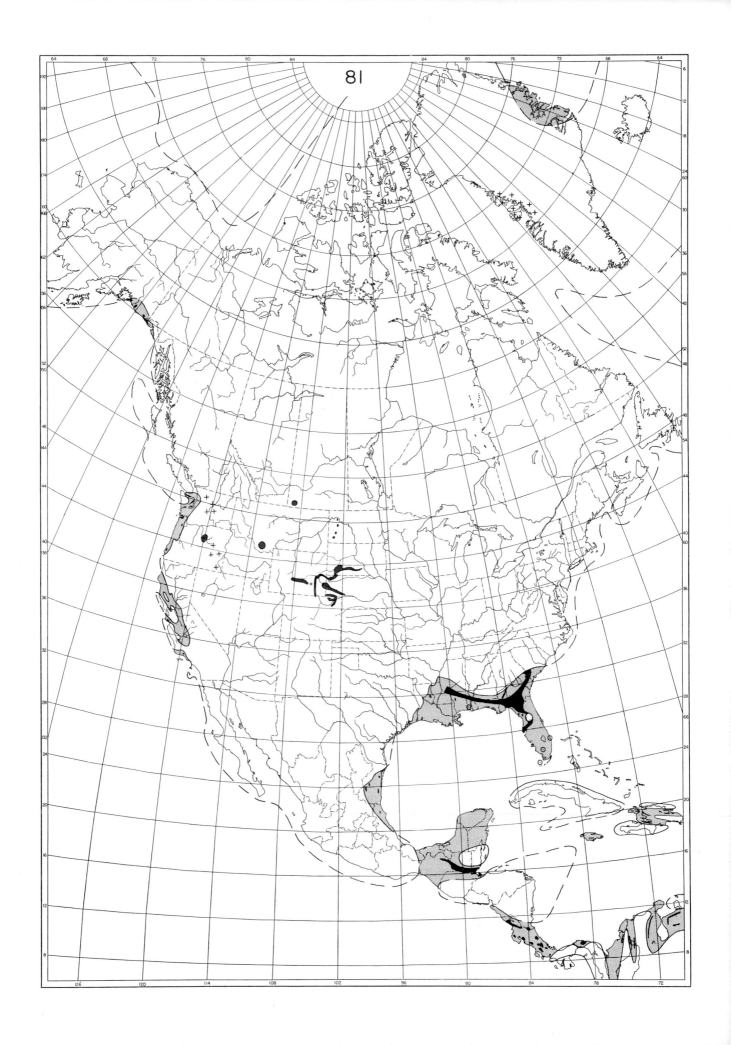

82

Middle Cenozoic
Miocene

STRATIGRAPHIC UNITS REPRESENTED

CALIFORNIA—Crocker Springs fm., Maricopa sh., Modelo fm., Monterey sh., Temblor fm., and Vaqueros fm.

CALIFORNIA, LOWER—Comondu fm. and Isidro fm.

FLORIDA—Alum Bluff gr., Choctawhatchee fm., Hawthorn fm., and Tampa ls.

GEORGIA—Hawthorn fm. and Tampa ls.

LOUISIANA—Catahoula ss., Hattiesburg clay, and Pascagoula clay

MISSISSIPPI—Catahoula ss., Hattiesburg clay, and Pascagoula clay

NEBRASKA—Arikaree gr. and Hemingsford gr.

NEW JERSEY—Kirkwood fm.

NEW MEXICO—Santa Fe fm. (basal part)

NORTH CAROLINA—St. Marys fm. and Yorktown fm.

OREGON—John Day fm. (middle and upper part) and Mascall fm.

SOUTH CAROLINA—Hawthorn fm. and Raysor marl

SOUTH DAKOTA—Bijou Hills fm. and Rosebud fm.

TEXAS—Catahoula ss., Lagarto clay, and Oakville ss.

VIRGINIA—Calvert fm., Choptank fm., St. Marys fm., and Yorktown fm.

———

COSTA RICA—Gatun fm.

DOMINICAN REPUBLIC—Baitoa fm., Cercado fm., Cerros de Sal fm., Cevicos ls., and Gurabo fm.

JAMAICA—Bowden fm.

PANAMA—Caimito fm., Emperador ls., and Gatun fm.

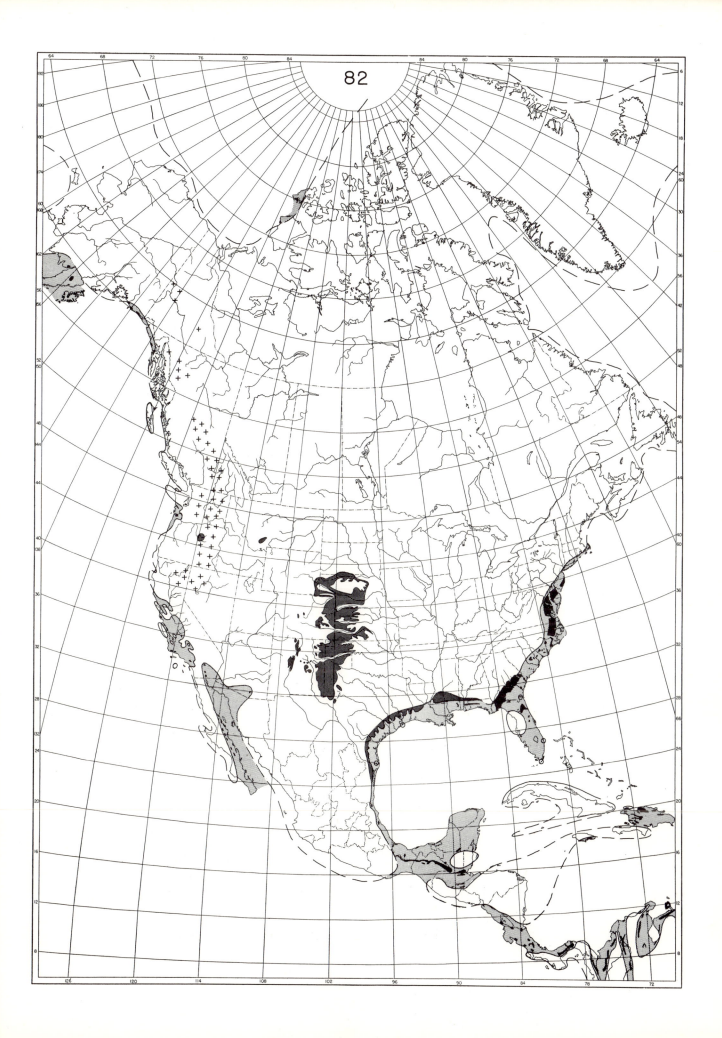

83

Upper Cenozoic
Pliocene

STRATIGRAPHIC UNITS REPRESENTED

ALABAMA—Citronelle fm.

CALIFORNIA—Etchegoin fm., Jacalitos fm., Purisima fm., and Repetto fm.

COLORADO—Ogallala gr.

FLORIDA—Alachua fm., Buckingham marl, Caloosahatchee fm., and Citronelle fm.

GEORGIA—Charlton fm.

KANSAS—Ogallala gr.

LOUISIANA—Citronelle fm.

MISSISSIPPI—Citronelle fm.

NEBRASKA—Ogallala gr.

NEVADA—Esmeralda fm. and Thousand Creek fm.

NEW MEXICO—Bidahochi fm. and Santa Fe fm.

NORTH CAROLINA—Croatan sand

OREGON—Ironside fm., Rattlesnake fm., and John Day fm.

SOUTH CAROLINA—Waccamaw fm.

TEXAS, NW.—Ogallala gr.

TEXAS, SE.—Goliad sand

WASHINGTON—Ellensburg fm. and Hagerman fm.

———

PANAMA—Chagres ss.

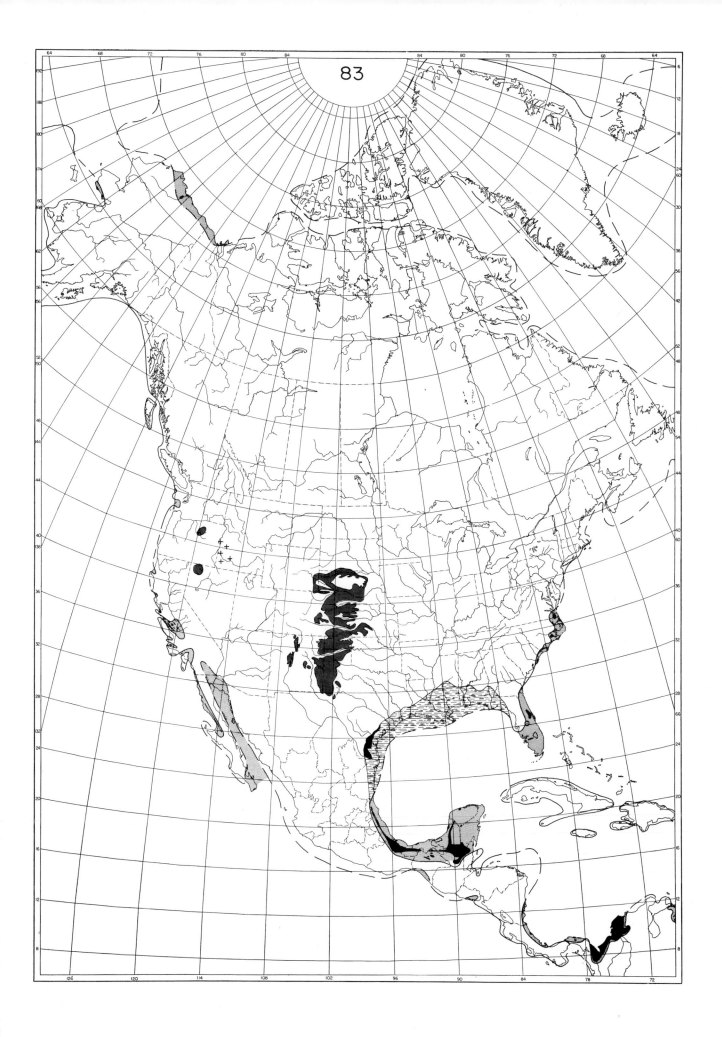

83

84

Highest Cenozoic

Pleistocene

STRATIGRAPHIC UNITS REPRESENTED

FLORIDA—Anastasia fm., Key Largo ls., Miami oolite, and Pamlico sand

NEW JERSEY—Cape May fm. and Pensauken fm.

NEW YORK, Long Island—Gardiners clay, Jacob sand, Manhasset fm., and Vineyard fm.

TEXAS—Beaumont clay and Lissie sand

———

CANADA, eastern—Champlain clay

Editor's note: Neither the glacial deposits nor the terrace gravels are shown on this map.

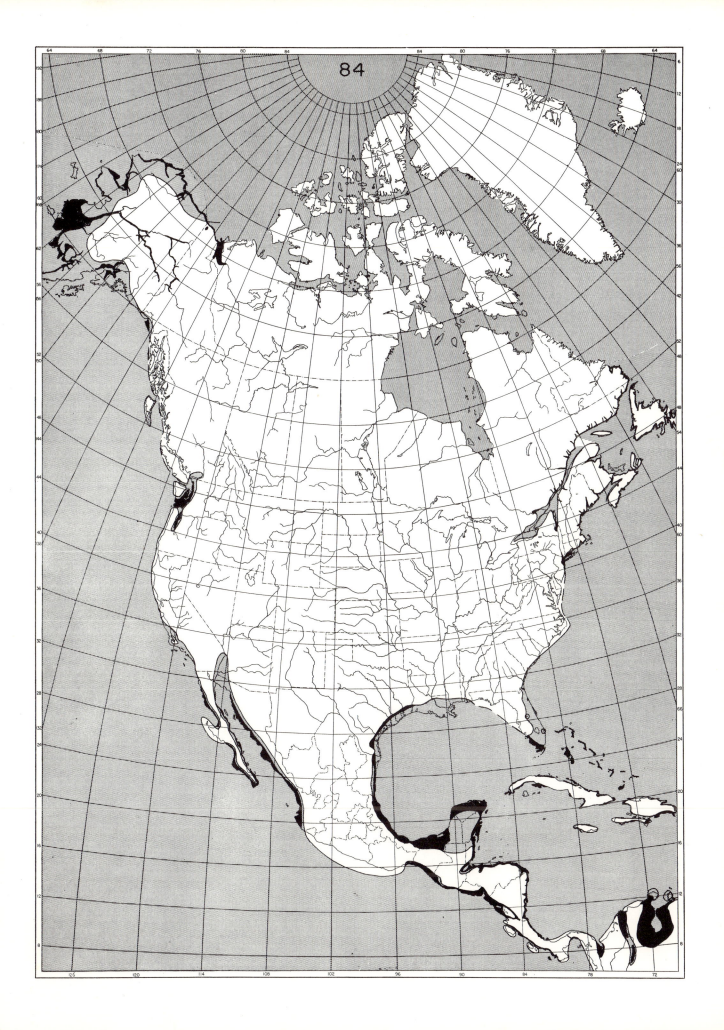

84

INDEX *

* Numbers in index refer to map numbers.

Presque Isle dol., 35
Price fm., 41, 42
Prospect Mountain qtzite., 2
Prosser ls., 15
Ptarmigan fm., 4
Pueblo fm., 55
Puerco fm., 77
Puget gr., 78
Purisima fm., 83
Put-in-Bay dol., 29
Putnam fm., 55

Quadrant fm., 49, 50, 51, 52
Quall ls., 32
Queenston sh., 20
Quoddy fm., 25

Racine dol., 27
Ragland ss., 35
Ramparts ls., 35
Ramshorn sl., 10
Ratcliff Brook fm., 3
Raton fm., 76
Rattlesnake fm., 83
Ravenscrag fm., 77
Raysor marl, 82
Reagan ss., 6
Red Mountain gr., 25
Red Mountain ss., 21, 22, 23, 24
Red River fm., 20
Redwall ls., 41, 44
Red Wash fm., 60, 61
Redwater sh., 67
Reeds Spring chert, 42
Reedsville sh., 17, 18
Relief qtzite., 45
Renault fm., 46
Repetto fm., 83
Ridgeley ss., 32
Ridley ls., 14
Rincon ls., 8
Rochester sh., 25
Rochester trachyte, 57
Rockdale dol., 25
Rockland ls., 15
Rogers City ls., 35
Rogers Spring ls., 41, 42
Rogersville sh., 5
Rome fm., 3
Rosebud fm., 82
Rose Hill sh., 24
Ross Brook fm., 24
Rugg Brook dol., 5
Rundle ls., 45, 46
Rutledge ls., 4

St. Albans sh., 31
St. Albans sl., 5
St. Charles fm., 7
St. Clair ls., 25
St. Edmund dol., 24
Ste. Genevieve ls., 45
St. George dol., 9, 10, 11
St. Joe ls., 42
St. Louis ls., 44

St. Mary River fm., 76
St. Marys fm., 82
St. Peter ss., 12, 13
St. Piran fm., 3
Salem ls., 44
Salina gr., 29
Salina fm., 29
Salona ls., 15
Salt Mountain ls., 78
Saltville chert, 33
Saluda fm., 20
Sample ss., 46
San Andres ls., 57
San Juan Raya fm., 70
San Juan gr., 52
San Lorenzo sh., 81
Sand Coulee fm., 78
Santa Fe fm., 82, 83
Santee ls., 80
Sarbach ls., 10, 11
Satanka sh., 56
Saturday Mountain dol., 20
Savanna fm., 51
Saverton sh., 39
Sawatch fm., 6
Schaghticoke sh., 9
Schenectady flags., 15
Schodack sh., 3
Schoharie sh., 33
Scotty Wash qtzite., 44, 45
Secret Canyon sh., 5
Sedalia ls., 41
Selinsgrove ls., 34
Sellersburg ls., 36
Selma chalk, 75
Sequatchie fm., 19, 20
Sespe fm., 80, 81
Severn River ls., 22
Sevier fm., 14
Sewanee ls., 81
Sextant fm., 34
Shady dol., 2
Shakopee dol., 10
Shammattawa ls., 20
Shark River marl, 79
Shasta fm., 72
Shawangunk cgl., 22, 23, 24, 25
Shell Rock ls., 38
Shenango fm., 42
Sherburne ss., 37
Sherman Fall ls., 15
Shochary ss., 18
Shuler fm., 69
Sierra Madre ls., 72
Signal Mountain ls., 8
Silica sh., 36
Silverhorn dol., 37
Simonson dol., 35
Simpson sh., 38
Skaneateles fm., 36
Skaneateles stage, 36
Skoki ls., 12
Skwentna gr., 65
Slave Point ls., 37

Sly Gap fm., 38
Smackover fm., 67
Smithville ls., 11
Snake Hill sh., 15
Sneedville ls., 25, 30
Snooks Arm fm., 10, 11
Snowy Range fm., 7
Snyder Creek sh., 37
Sparta sand, 79
Spearfish fm., 57
Speeds ls., 35
Spergen ls., 44
Spotted Ridge fm., 52
Spray River fm., 60
Springer fm., 49
Springvale fm., 33
Square Lake ls., 31
Squaw Bay ls., 37
Stanbridge sl., 15, 16
Steamboat ls., 5
Steele sh., 75
Stephen fm., 5
Stirling qtzite., 2
Stonefort ls., 51
Stonehenge ls., 9
Stonehouse fm., 28, 29, 30
Stony Mountain fm., 20
Stony Point sh., 15
Strawn series, 51, 52
Strites Pond ls., 9
Stuhini gr., 63
Sullivan fm., 6
Sultan ls., 37
Summerville fm., 67
Sumner gr., 56
Sunbury sh., 40
Sundance fm., 67
Sunrise fm., 65
Supai fm., 53, 56
Suspension Bridge dol., 27
Swan Peak qtzite., 12
Swasey fm., 5
Swearinger sl., 64
Swift fm., 67
Switchback fm., 5
Sylamore ss., 39

Tabera fm., 81
Tah fm., 2
Takla gr., 63
Talisman qtzite., 49
Talkeetna fm., 65
Tallahatta fm., 79
Tamaulipas ls., 70, 72
Tampa ls., 82
Tanyard fm., 9
Tapo Ranch fm., 79
Tar Springs ss., 48
Tatei fm., 4
Tatina gr., 12
Tatow ls., 3
Taylor marl, 75
Temblor fm., 82